40P

THE DEVIL IN COMMAND

D0718294

The only way Stacey could get the
formidable Paul Leandros to leave her
young sister alone was to divert his
attention to herself—which she succeeded in doing, with a vengeance! For
Paul's price was that she marry him,
and, far too late, Stacey realised that
the price was too high for her to pay
and keep her emotions intact...

Books you will enjoy
by HELEN BIANCHIN

MASTER OF ULURU

On a working holiday in Australia, Janie found herself encountering the forceful Logan more often than was good for her peace of mind. She could not deny his attraction—but did he want anything from her but a transient pleasure and amusement? After all, what did she know about him?

EDGE OF SPRING

After a brief and desperately disillusioning marriage, Karen had managed to keep all men at bay for five years. But she was having rather more trouble with Matt Lucas, who refused to take no for an answer. How could she convince him that she didn't want to have anything to do with him, ever?

STORMY POSSESSION

Marry Luke Andretti—or let her father go bankrupt: that was the agonising choice facing Sally Bellinger. And Luke had made it clear that it was to be a real marriage, because he wanted a son. So what could she do but accept? But then she found herself gradually falling in love with her husband. Would her pride ever allow her to admit it?

THE VINES IN SPLENDOUR

Life wasn't too easy for Shannon, with a little niece to support and not very much money— and things weren't made any easier by the constant, exasperating presence of Nick Stanich. He knew she didn't like him, he couldn't possibly be serious about her—why on earth couldn't he leave her alone?

DEVIL IN COMMAND

BY
HELEN BIANCHIN

MILLS & BOON LIMITED
15–16 BROOK'S MEWS
LONDON W1A 1DR

All the characters in this book have no existence outside the imagination of the Author, and have no relation whatsoever to anyone bearing the same name or names. They are not even distantly inspired by any individual known or unknown to the Author, and all the incidents are pure invention.

The text of this publication or any part thereof may not be reproduced or transmitted in any form or by any means, electronic or mechanical, including photocopying, recording, storage in an information retrieval system, or otherwise, without the written permission of the publisher.

This book is sold subject to the condition that it shall not, by way of trade or otherwise, be lent, resold, hired out or otherwise circulated without the prior consent of the publisher in any form of binding or cover other than that in which it is published and without a similar condition including this condition being imposed on the subsequent purchaser.

First published 1980
Australian copyright 1981
Philippine copyright 1981
This edition 1981

© Helen Bianchin 1980

ISBN 0 263 73420 X

Set in Linotype Baskerville 10 on 11½ pt.

Made and printed in Great Britain by
Richard Clay (The Chaucer Press), Ltd., Bungay, Suffolk

CHAPTER ONE

STACEY skirted one of several yawning puddles as she crossed the busy city intersection, and on reaching the pavement she hastily sought cover beneath a sheltering shop verandah.

It was one of the coldest, wettest days to befall Melbourne this winter, she decided ruefully as she surveyed her windswept reflection in an adjacent shop window. The glance was a cursory one, for she had few pretensions about her own beauty, conscious only of a slimly-curved figure, well-defined features and wavy chestnut shoulder-length hair.

The task ahead of her wasn't a pleasant one, and on reaching the multi-storied office block she entered the downstairs foyer and paused in contemplative silence as she checked the directory plaque.

The Leandros Corporation had their offices on the fifteenth floor, and she summoned the elevator, jabbing the button with unnecessary force. She was more than ready to do battle—it showed in the proud lift of her chin, the fiery sparkle in her green-flecked hazel eyes.

Stepping across the plush carpet to the reception desk Stacey met the faintly enquiring glance directed her, and countered it coolly. 'Paul Leandros—I'd like to see him, please.'

The receptionist's face became an efficient mask. 'Mr Leandros is in conference. What time is your appointment?'

'I don't have one,' Stacey stated baldly. 'However,

I'm sure he'll see me.' She forced a confident smile, adding with slight emphasis, 'Miss Armitage.'

Momentary hesitation clouded the receptionist's features. 'I'll ring through to Mr Leandros' secretary and confirm when the conference is expected to conclude.'

Minutes later Stacey was escorted along a wide passageway whose walls were adorned at regularly spaced intervals with conservative prints, and ensconced in a luxuriously appointed room commanding a superb view over the South Yarra River, she sought to calm her frayed temper by leafing through the variety of magazines placed at her disposal.

Time ticked relentlessly by as fifteen minutes progressed to thirty, and it was almost an hour before she was summoned to meet the exalted head of the diverse financial organisation.

Nothing, not even Trisha's rapt and frequent eulogies, prepared Stacey for the leashed power the man emanated. Of Greek descent, he had the height, the broad-chiselled almost saturnine features of his ancestors, eyes as black as ebony in a face that was startlingly rugged. A truly formidable male animal, and a dangerous one, she perceived. It was there in his bearing—a ruthlessness clearly evident, forbidding and faintly cruel.

'Miss Armitage?' His voice was deep, its inflection faintly arrogant, yet chillingly polite, and she suppressed a slight shiver of apprehension.

'Stacey Armitage—Trisha's sister,' she informed him with deliberate significance.

One eyebrow arched in silent query. 'There is something I can do for you?'

'I haven't come here to exchange polite conversation, Mr Leandros,' Stacey sallied resentfully.

'Precisely why have you come, Miss Armitage?' he questioned with marked cynicism, his gaze disconcertingly direct.

'You don't deny that you know Trisha?' she demanded, her eyes brilliant with barely suppressed animosity.

'I am acquainted with your sister—yes,' he responded evenly, and Stacey gave a derisory laugh.

'Oh, really, Mr Leandros—*acquaintance* is too mild a word, surely?'

'Association, perhaps?'

'*Affair* would be more apt,' she condemned wrathfully.

His gaze didn't falter as he withdrew a slim cigarette case and lighter, extracting a thin cheroot and placing it between his lips, then lighting it before choosing to speak.

'That's almost an allegation,' he stated slowly as he exhaled a thin spiral of smoke. 'I trust you are certain of your facts?'

Stacey drew a deep breath, then released it slowly. 'Mr Leandros,' she began, tight-lipped, 'how old do you imagine my sister is?'

He gave a slight shrug, the action both indolent and uncaring. 'Is it of any significance?'

'Damn you—*yes*!' she snapped furiously.

'Aren't you taking this a little too seriously?' Paul Leandros queried sardonically. 'Your parents—surely it's they who should evince any concern?'

'My parents are dead,' Stacey stated repressively. 'I'm all Trisha has by way of family.'

'Ah—I see. You seek to play the role of protector,' he concluded with thinly veiled cynicism.

Oh, he was *amused*, she determined wrathfully. In a minute she'd be goaded into slapping his hateful face! Summoning every ounce of calm, she demanded, 'Precisely how old do you imagine my sister is, Mr Leandros?'

'Nineteen—twenty,' he hazarded indolently. 'Old enough, I think?'

The stinging slap sounded loud in the silence of the room—a silence that lengthened until it became almost a tangible entity.

Stacey met his penetrating gaze unflinchingly, undaunted by the shaft of gleaming anger in the dark eyes several inches above her own.

'Do that again,' Paul Leandros cautioned grimly, 'and I can promise retaliatory action.'

'You dare to threaten me?'

His ebony gaze left her face and swept slowly down to her elegantly shod feet, then back again. 'Do you doubt it?'

A shiver feathered its way down her spine, and she had to enforce control against it becoming visible. 'Aren't there sufficient women available from which to choose a suitable—companion, Mr Leandros?' she queried with deliberate emphasis. 'Or have they palled to the extent that you must pursue a sixteen-year-old girl who hasn't the sense not to date a man old enough to be her father!'

Anger flared briefly, then became masked as his eyelids lowered fractionally. 'Be very careful of the accusations you fling in my direction, Miss Armitage,' he drawled icily, 'or I may consider I have just cause to sue for defamation.'

Fury sparked in her eyes, bringing them vibrantly alive as she glared up at him. 'Perhaps *I* should sue *you* for attempting to tamper with an innocent *child*!'

'By the living heaven,' Paul Leandros breathed emotively, 'you tempt me to the very brink of reasonable patience!' A fist smote against the palm of his hand in a single explosive action that caused Stacey to start involuntarily. 'Consider it prudent to leave—now.' He crossed to the door and opened it.

'Will you refrain from seeing Trisha?' she persisted, and was chilled by his grim implacability.

'Goodbye, Miss Armitage,' he concluded bluntly, and she could have hit him from sheer angry frustration.

Lifting her chin fractionally, Stacey swept past him, moving quickly down the passageway and out through reception to the elevator.

Paul Leandros was certainly a force to be reckoned with, she grimaced wryly some five minutes later as she slipped behind the wheel of her small car and set it in motion, heading it north towards Essendon. They had struck sparks off each other from the onset, and instead of gaining his support she had only succeeded in antagonising him.

Looking after Trisha was a responsibility Stacey had willingly shouldered for the past six years. Almost eight years separated them in age, but there were times when Stacey felt a veritable Methuselah in the face of Trisha's frequent outbursts. Childish misdemeanours had developed into scrapes that had at times been serious enough to warrant dire warnings of possible expulsion from the school's headmistress. An apt but lazy scholar, Trisha had emerged on to the employment scene last year, and much to Stacey's relief, it seemed the acquisition of a pay packet at the end of each week was sufficient enticement for Trisha to remain one of the working force.

Trisha's liaison with an older man was merely the latest in a series of harassing incidents Stacey had had to contend with, and during the past few weeks she had cajoled, pleaded and alternately raged, in an effort to make her sister see reason, becoming embroiled in all too frequent scenes that were both nerve-racking and soul-destroying. Anything remotely approaching conversation between them had ceased almost a week ago, and since then they had resorted to brief messages of essential importance hastily penned and magnetically anchored to the refrigerator door.

That one man should be the cause of so much agony was beyond Stacey's comprehension and endurance, and this morning she had decided the matter had gone far enough.

Now she had to concede that her attempt to alleviate the situation had been a dismal failure. The only consolation she had was that Paul Leandros was now aware of Trisha's correct age, and it was possible that on reflection he might have second thoughts about continuing the relationship. It was a dim hope, but one she clung to as she parked her Mini in the space allotted employees inside the hospital gates.

Working as a physiotherapist was a challenging occupation which Stacey found totally absorbing. For the past two years she had been assigned to the Royal Children's Hospital, and working with children gave her a rare insight to their tenacity to overcome insurmountable odds.

Entering the side entrance, she made her way to the physiotherapy department, checked with the office which ward she was to go to, then took the elevator to Surgical.

There were three new faces, drowsy and pale from the effects of anaesthetic, and she moved to the first of her patients, greeted him by name, then began coaxing him gently to exert his limbs and effect breathing exercises.

It was after six when Stacey inserted the key into the

front door of the flat she shared with Trisha. Comfortably furnished, it was in a block of three situated in a pleasant tree-lined street within reasonable access to the city.

There was no visible sign that Trisha had been home, and Stacey drew in a deep breath, her brow creasing slightly as a familiar feeling of anxiety rose to the fore. Wearily she set about preparing a meal—for two, just in case Trisha put in an appearance—then she sat down and ate alone, willing the phone to ring as the evening progressed.

It was after eleven when she switched on the porch light and prepared for bed, and she was about to slip between the covers when the insistent peal from the phone in the hallway sent her flying to answer it.

'Stacey! Thank God!' Trisha's voice declared with pious disregard. 'Can you come and pick me up?'

Stacey fought down the feeling of resigned frustration. 'Where are you?' she managed calmly.

'The hospital. Don't panic,' Trisha added quickly. 'I'm okay. There was an accident—not bad, but the ambulance attendant insisted I be medically examined before coming home.' She quickly gave the name of the hospital, then hung up before Stacey had the chance to say anything.

Twenty minutes later she presented herself at the accident and emergency ward, and was greeted by a subdued Trisha looking remarkably healthy and bearing no outward sign of any injury.

'I'm okay—really,' Trisha assured her, then declared hastily, 'Let's get out of here. This place gives me the shivers!'

It didn't occur to Stacey to question her sister's expressed urgency to leave the hospital or its grounds, and it wasn't until three days later that the real reason unfolded itself by way of a terse legally-phrased letter.

The contents horrified her, as did the strongly emblazoned signature at the lower edge of the page, and she sank into a nearby chair, too stunned to do anything, until returning sanity and an unreasoning anger brought her to her feet.

Crossing to the telephone, she hurriedly looked up the number she wanted, then dialled the necessary digits, her lips tightening as she heard Trisha's voice, bright and carefree, at the other end of the phone. Without preamble she queried starkly:

'The car you were in the other night—were you driving it?'

'Stacey?' Trisha's voice rose querulously. 'What's the matter? Is something wrong?'

Catching a tight rein on her temper, she clutched the receiver, the blood cold in her veins. 'Cut out the word-play, Trisha,' she advised curtly. 'This is serious. Were you driving the car?'

'Oh, Stacey, you know I haven't got a licence. How could I possibly be driving?'

'Nothing you do would surprise me,' Stacey said heavily. 'But this—if it's true, is the most reprehensible of any of your escapades. Now, were you driving that car?'

There was a long silence at the other end, then Trisha admitted reluctantly, 'Well, yes. But only for a few minutes——'

'That's long enough,' Stacey returned darkly. 'Trisha, how could you be so *stupid*! You know darned well that without a learner's permit you shouldn't have been driving *any* car.'

'It seemed like a fun idea at the time,' Trisha declared sulkily. 'I can't understand why you're making so much fuss—no one was hurt.'

Stacey almost exploded. 'Dear God, you're priceless! I suppose you think that exonerates you from any blame. Did you consider the damage to the car you were illegally driving? Or the car you hit?' Her voice rose a full octave. 'What about that, Trisha?'

'Oh, for heaven's sake! Insurance- will cover it, won't it?'

'Whose?' Stacey responded succinctly. 'You don't even have any idea of the consequences, do you?'

'What consequences? What are you talking about?'

'I have a letter from Paul Leandros citing damages to the car you hit for an unspecified amount, and commanding my presence in his office tomorrow morning to discuss it.'

A breathless silence greeted this information, then Trisha said faintly, 'From *Paul*?'

'Yes—*Paul*,' Stacey echoed with emphasis. 'There isn't anything else I should be aware of before I see him, I suppose?'

'You make it sound like a crime,' Trisha complained petulantly, and Stacey momentarily closed her eyes in a silent prayer for patience.

'It is a crime—make no mistake about it. I've pulled you out of many a scrape, but I'm not sure I can manage to do it this time.'

'Stacey, I have to go. I am at work, you know,' Trisha said with a long-drawn-out sigh. 'I'll see you later.'

'You do intend coming home tonight, then?'

'I'm not sure. Pam wants me to stay over. You don't mind do you?'

Would it matter if I did? Stacey questioned silently,

knowing that to argue would prove fruitless. 'Make sure you're here tomorrow when I get home,' she added hardily.

'Okay. Good luck,' Trisha said hastily, and replaced the receiver before Stacey had a chance to say anything else.

Luck wouldn't help much, it was more like a miracle she needed, Stacey decided as she entered the portals of the exalted Leandros Corporation the following morning. Within minutes she was shown into the waiting room adjoining Paul Leandros' executive suite.

Nerves twisted her stomach into a painful knot as she contemplated her last encounter with the hateful businessman, and it took all her resolve to present a calm exterior as she entered his office.

'You wanted to see me, Mr Leandros?' she queried steadily, coming to a standstill a few feet from his desk.

Paul Leandros turned from his appraisal of the street below the expanse of plate-glass and slowly raked her from head to toe. He looked dynamic and infinitely masculine, his sober business suit barely detracting from a raw virility that was frightening.

'You are responsible for your sister, are you not?' he demanded silkily, and Stacey uttered a brief affirmative in response. 'I trust you have spoken with her since receiving my letter?'

'Yes.' The monosyllabic admission was tautly delivered.

He moved slightly, thrusting one hand into his trouser pocket, his gaze unwavering. 'I would be interested to hear what she had to say.'

Stacey braced her shoulders, her expression becoming faintly defensive. 'Trisha admits she was driving the car.'

'Nothing else?' he parried with deceptive calm.

'She doesn't have a licence,' she informed him stiltedly, and saw his faint grimace.

'Not only does your sister not have a licence, Miss Armitage,' he said softly, 'she doesn't even possess a learner's permit. You are, of course, aware of that?'

'Of course I am,' Stacey expostulated. 'Suppose you stop fencing around, and come straight to the point.'

'There's more,' Paul Leandros stated with studied indolence, his eyes glittering like polished onyx. 'My nephew borrowed the car without my permission—the reason being, I gather, to impress your sister.' He paused slightly, then continued, 'By means I won't elaborate, your sister managed to persuade him to part with the keys, although it is perhaps to his credit that he immediately had second thoughts and attempted to retrieve them.' His glance speared her ruthlessly. 'Unfortunately, he was unable to do so. Your sister foolishly ignored any injunction, and proceeded to drive off at high speed.'

'I see,' Stacey managed in slightly strangled tones.

'Do you, Miss Armitage?' he queried with intended sarcasm. 'The owner of the Lotus Elan intends to sue for negligence,' he continued dryly. 'That amount, coupled with damages to his car, totals an exorbitant sum.' He named a figure that was staggering and Stacey gasped, her expressive features whitening with shock.

'You can't be serious?'

His smile was grim. 'There is also the matter of misappropriation of my Ferrari. Theft is a serious charge.'

'You would charge your own nephew?' she questioned with incredulity.

'Your sister, Miss Armitage.'

'Dear God,' she whispered, her eyes wide with horror, 'can you imagine what that will do to her?' The thought was inconceivable! Desperately clutching at straws, she beseeched, 'if it takes everything I have, I'll come up with the amount required. Surely some agreement can be reached as to punitive damages?' Her brain raced with rapidly assembled figures. 'I have a savings account—there's my car——'

'You haven't considered your loyalty may be misplaced?'

'However much Trisha needs to be made aware of her wrongdoing, I can't stand aside and see her taken to court. Even if it means realising every asset I have!'

'And if your total assets prove to be insufficient?'

'I'll plead for time.'

'What makes you think I would be agreeable?' Paul Leandros queried with uncompromising bleakness. 'Less than a week ago you were insultingly rude, as well as resorting to physical assault.'

Stacey fought for control, her eyes flashing green fire. 'I was provoked,' she alleged tightly, and saw his jaw muscles tighten measurably.

'Do you imagine I was not?'

'Oh for heaven's sake!' she exploded. 'How did you expect me to react? You've been squiring my sister around town for more than a month—a sixteen-year-old girl not six months out of school! God knows, Trisha is difficult enough to handle. When I couldn't get anywhere with her, I had little option other than to contact you.'

He regarded her silently for what seemed an interminable length of time, and she could gather little from his harsh expression. His eyes never left hers for a second, and she began to feel mesmerised—akin to the prey awaiting the strike from a deadly snake!

'*I* have been escorting your sister?' Paul Leandros queried with dangerous softness. 'You have proof of such an allegation, Miss Armitage?'

'Trisha told me——'

'Ah, yes—Trisha.' His eyes hardened. 'That young lady appears to have a lot to answer for.'

The first frightening seeds of doubt and their resultant implication were reflected momentarily, and a slight frown creased her brow as she tried to assimilate exactly what he meant. 'She's dined with you, been to your home——'

'Correction,' he said silkily. 'Your sister has dined twice in my company—once as part of a family group at my home, and once by chance in a city restaurant. On both occasions she was escorted by my nephew.'

Angry incredulous words tumbled from her lips. 'Are you telling me the truth?'

'You would accuse me of lying?' he countered dangerously, and Stacey's gaze wavered.

'I don't understand,' she faltered, badly shaken. 'Trisha never once mentioned your nephew's name.'

'A question of deliberate delusion, I imagine.' He turned slightly, moving to the wide glass window, and stood seemingly engrossed with movement on the street below.

After a long silence Stacey offered quietly, 'I owe you an apology.'

'Mere words won't suffice, Miss Armitage.' His tone was chillingly direct, and Stacey felt her heart plummet as she glimpsed his humourless smile.

'Business and sentiment don't mix—or are you unaware of that analogy?'

She swallowed painfully, meeting his raking gaze with a mixture of hopeless anger. 'I take it from that, you aren't prepared to be lenient?'

'I am of Greek descent,' Paul Leandros elaborated with deliberate emphasis. 'Revenge for an aggrievance is considered arbitrary.'

'Revenge? What are you talking about?' she cried, unable to believe him.

'Your total assets,' he countered relentlessly. 'A car —a savings account. What else?'

Her head lifted fractionally, pride uppermost. 'A few shares.'

'But not, I suspect, enough to cover total damages,' he deduced hardily. 'What other form of recompense would you suggest?'

'I have no other assets,' she reiterated, and saw his eyes narrow as he toyed idly with a paperweight on top of his desk.

'You do not consider yourself as an asset?'

Anger almost tantamount to sheer blinding rage erupted inside her. 'Precisely what do you mean?'

His smile was wholly cynical. 'Come, Miss Armitage, you can't be that naïve.'

Her face suffused with delicate colour, then paled as the significance of his words took effect. 'You think I'd trade sex as payment?' she choked, her eyes brilliant with fury. 'Never in a million years!'

One eyebrow lifted slightly. 'So adamant,' he chided softly, the velvet-smooth tones sending a frisson of fear down her spine, making her shiver involuntarily. He considered her thoughtfully. 'Taming all that latent emotion could prove an intriguing exercise.'

'Forget it—you'll never have the opportunity!'

His laugh was a silent one, his eyes dark with sardonic humour. 'Oh, but I shall.' He moved round to lean against the edge of his desk, his expression assuming brooding implacability. 'As my wife you would become an asset,' he elaborated. 'Legally bound, affording a tangible measure of payment.'

'You've got to be mad! I wouldn't marry you if you were the last man on earth!'

Paul Leandros' eyes became ebony-hard as they bored relentlessly across the space between them. 'Think yourself fortunate I offer marriage.'

'Why?' Stacey flung with asperity. 'Am I supposed to swoon with relief?' She let her eyes run the length of his imposing frame. 'I'm not for sale,' she declared succinctly.

Slowly he withdrew a packet of cheroots, extracted one and placed it between his lips, then lit it with indolent deliberation, exhaling the smoke with evident satisfaction before regarding her. 'Think carefully,' he warned with silky detachment. 'Once you step outside this room your decision will be irreversible.'

Stacey experienced a clutch of fear and her brain began spiralling with the implications his threat aroused. Slowly she queried, 'How sure are you that the other complainant will drop charges?'

'Money—sufficient of it,' he added cynically, 'has a way of soothing even the most indignant of men.'

She struggled against a rapidly rising temper. 'You really know how to lay it on the line, don't you?' Her voice rose as she accused, 'Coercion is a crime, Mr Leandros.'

'Oh, come, I much prefer persuasion,' he drawled, and she retaliated blindly,

'It could almost be termed extortion! Dear God, you're detestable. I hate you!'

'Hate as much as you like,' he drawled with implacable calm.

'My sister's freedom in exchange for mine,' she said heavily, then tilted her head to one side. 'Even a condemned prisoner is acquainted with the term of his sentence. How long, Mr Leandros?'

'Considering the amount involved,' he deliberated, raking her stormy features, 'two years should be sufficient.'

'I'll make sure they're as hellish as I can make them,' she vowed tightly.

'Revenge, Stacey?' Paul Leandros mocked.

'If I had a knife, I think I could kill you!' she retorted, and was enraged when he laughed.

'I consider myself forewarned.'

At such blatant mockery she threw the nearest thing at hand—her leather shoulder-bag—and watched him field it neatly and place it down on top of his desk.

'Come and get it,' he insisted with dangerous softness, reaching out and catching hold of her hand. With seemingly little effort he exerted sufficient pressure to pull her out of the chair towards him, bringing her close despite the struggles she made.

'Leave me alone!' she snapped furiously.

'Like a child you hit out, then cry when the action is about to be reciprocated. You'd prefer me to act the gentleman, perhaps?'

'You're a fiend!' Stacey flung, becoming breathless as she tried to escape his steel-like grasp.

'You have no knowledge what manner of man I am, yet you hurl insults as if they were merely words of no importance. Guard your tongue, Stacey, or you may very well have reason for such accusations.'

'I loathe and destest you—think of that when you try to——'

'Bed you? Be assured that I shall—frequently.'

'Of course,' Stacey threw incautiously, 'I must remember to keep a count. Be warned I don't come cheap!'

His eyes hardened until they resembled polished onyx, then he drew her inexorably forward until her breasts pressed against the buttons of his waistcoat. In slow motion one hand slid to fasten a hold at her nape as the other moved down the length of her spine, moulding her close so that she was shockingly aware of his physical hardness, the pressure of his powerful thighs.

'You want me to exact the first payment now—*here*?'

The query was quiet and deadly, and Stacey sensed his temper was held in check by a tenuous thread. Yet still she refused to capitulate completely. 'I don't imagine you would be so—animalistic,' she gasped, then cried out as his hands tightened painfully. 'You're hurting me!'

With an angry oath he flung her away from him. 'Get out of my sight,' he directed harshly, lifting an arm and raking a hand through his hair, then he thrust it into a trouser pocket and turned back towards his desk. 'I'll contact you as soon as suitable arrangements have been made.'

Stacey stood still, breathing hard, fear and dislike twisting her attractive features, then without a word she turned and walked to the door, not pausing to spare him so much as a backward glance.

CHAPTER TWO

THE wedding ceremony was brief and impersonal, the weather providing a cold bleak mantle that served only to accentuate the bizzare necessity of her union with the formidable Greek.

Attired in a superbly-tailored grey suit, Paul Leandros towered head and shoulders above her, his expression relaxed and totally in antithesis of Stacey's solemnity.

It seemed impossible so many arrangements had been made within the space of two days, yet they had, and it rankled terribly that she had not been consulted over one of them. Even her resignation at the hospital had been handled by Paul, and she could sense that systematically he was assuming command of her life.

She had been tempted not to buy a new dress for the occasion, but at the last moment she had given in and rushed into the city, selecting at random a light woollen cream suit, new shoes and a handbag.

Trisha, with typical teenage disregard, had displayed initial surprise, then complete unconcern at the news, and the fact that Stacey's marriage to Paul Leandros had come about solely for her benefit brought little more than a dismissive shrug.

The reception was a surprisingly formal affair held in the large dining-room of Paul's luxurious home in the prestigious suburb of Kew.

It was a family affair, the guests numbered almost twenty, and Stacey's brain reeled as she endeavoured to recall all their names. She blamed shock at discovering Paul had a son from a previous marriage for the numbness which seemed to freeze her usually mobile features into a permanent smile. Nicos was a boy the image of his father, looking somewhat older than his fifteen years, resplendent in an expensively-cut suit and immaculate shirt linen. Whether it was the combination of private schooling or strict parental control, there was polite charm and sincerity evident, a desire to be on friendly terms with his new step-mother that was disarming. Nicos bore none of the signs of teenage awkwardness, and Stacey clung to his friendship as a drowning man to a solitary life raft.

On the surface, convention was observed with re-markable dedication, the meal comprising no less than five courses with wine aplenty and a bridal toast with imported vintage champagne. There was even an in-intricately-iced wedding cake which was cut in the traditional manner and handed among the guests to-gether with sugared almonds.

All too soon coffee was served, and then one by one the family members began to disperse. Stacey was scarcely aware of Trisha's departure, or that Nicos had left with his grandmother. With alarming clarity she realised she was alone with the tall, magnificently arresting man standing less than three feet distant.

Nervously she twisted the wide diamond-studded platinum wedding ring on her finger, and for a brief few seconds she considered making an escape, then was forced to discard it in the certain knowledge that Paul Leandros would search until he found her, and the consequences of such an action proved a suitable de-terrent.

'More champagne?'

Stacey turned slightly and met Paul's dark sardonic gaze. 'Yes—why not?' She watched idly as he filled a

glass and then she took it from him to sip the contents with concerted dedication.

'You seem to share an affinity with my son,' Paul
drawled, placing the bottle back on to the table.

'Nicos appears to be a charming boy,' she responded
evenly.

'Unlike his father, hm?'

'Totally.'

'You were very quiet this evening,' he observed
with thinly veiled mockery, and she retaliated swiftly:

'I do possess a modicum of good manners.'

'But now that we are alone, they can be discarded—
is that it?'

Stacey met his gaze stoically. 'I'd rather be anywhere else than here with you. Would you prefer me
to pretend to be enraptured with delight?'

'It would help if you were amenable.'

'Well, I'm not,' she declared heatedly. 'Having to
bear you touch me will be sheer torture.'

'I have yet to kiss you,' he revealed cynically. 'You
may find you enjoy the experience.'

'Like hell,' she said inelegantly, and he laughed.

'Perhaps we should find out.'

'I fail to see what satisfaction you'll derive,' she said
desperately, grasping at any straw available. 'It's not
even acceptable that you should.'

For several seconds he observed her through slightly
narrowed lids, then he gave an eloquent shrug. 'If
what you imply is true——'

'Do you doubt me?' she countered angrily.

'I am acquainted with a woman's biological functions,' Paul inclined dryly.

'Then perhaps you'll be good enough to show me
to my room,' Stacey suggested coolly.

'Of course, if that is what you want.'

Relief washed over her, and she drained her glass, placing it down on to a nearby table before following him from the room.

A staircase curved upwards from the foyer to the floor above, and Stacey walked silently at his side, pausing to precede him as he held open a door at the end of the hallway.

Her eyes flicked to the large double bed with its embossed brocade counterpane, then moved in a slow encompassing arc over the mahogany furniture, the brocade drapes covering an entire wall back to the solitary illumination from the bedside lamp.

'The bathroom is through that door,' Paul informed her, moving an explanatory arm to his left. 'You'll find everything you need. Sophie will have unpacked your clothes, and I imagine it won't be difficult for you to discover their whereabouts.'

'Thank you.' Stacey moved towards the wardrobe and opened one of the doors, then ignoring his presence she crossed to the dressing-table and pulled open a succession of drawers, selecting what she needed, then she made for the bathroom, closing the door firmly behind her.

Within minutes she had discarded her clothes, and stepped beneath the warm spray of water, a sigh of relief on her lips that her ruse had succeeded. At least she had gained a few nights' grace from her husband's dreaded attentions.

Reaching for the soap, she began washing herself, luxuriating in the feel of the water on her body, the delicately scented fragrance that assailed her nostrils as she lathered.

The almost silent click of the door was barely detectable above the cascading water, and it was a sense of movement rather than noise that alerted Stacey's attention, causing her to glance beyond the folding glass screen of the shower stall.

The sight of Paul, divested of his clothes and naked except for a towel hitched strategically about his hips, brought forth a gasp of pure outrage.

'What are you doing? Get out!'

'This is my home—or have you forgotten?' Paul derided mockingly, letting his dark gaze wander over her slim curves with indolent ease.

Stacey hugged her arms across her breasts as colour suffused her face, and her eyes flashed with indignation. 'Have you no decency?' she cried, mortified. 'Am I to be permitted no privacy? Dear God, what manner of savage brute are you!' she ended with a scandalised screech as he folded back the door and stepped in beside her.

'A man who has bought two years of your life,' he stated austerely, and shock slithered down her spine at the pitiless deliberation in the dark eyes regarding her. 'I could almost be gulled into believing male nudity is a new experience for you. Why the act of modesty? As a physiotherapist and masseuse, you must admit the naked flesh holds no surprises, hm?'

'I worked in a children's hospital,' Stacey defended, her eyes averted from the riveting muscular frame so close in proximity. 'Will you please let me out?' Her voice rose a fraction. 'This may be your idea of fun, but it's not mine!'

'Really? You'd have me believe you've never shared a shower with a man?' he taunted. 'At twenty-four, in today's permissive society?'

'Believe what you like!' she threw angrily, and attempted to move past him. 'Will you let me out?'

His eyes held mocking cynicism. 'In so much of a hurry to go to bed?'

'I hate you!' she vowed furiously, tears of helpless frustration welling to the surface. 'God, I must have been mad to have married you!'

'You had no choice, remember?'

'You gave me no choice,' she corrected bitterly. Anger overrode her embarrassment. 'I loathe and detest you!'

A sardonic gleam of amusement slanted downwards. 'So much hatred,' he drawled. 'Do you imagine I'll leave you alone tonight, or any other night?'

Bleak dejection settled like a shroud over her shoulders. 'No.' Her eyes met his unflinchingly. 'You bought my body—to use, and probably abuse. I hope it sticks like bitter gall in your throat that nothing you can do will make me enjoy it.' She slipped past him only to be brought to an abrupt halt. Fear aroused a deep curling sensation in the pit of her stomach, and she lashed out at him, striking his chest with flailing fists, making little impression on that rock-hard sinewy wall.

Her wrists were caught and held together with effortless ease, his expression wholly cynical as he regarded her. 'So great a fuss you create—like an outraged virgin about to be raped.'

'That's what you intend, so why bother denying it?' Stacey flung, her breath ragged in her throat.

'You're not above inventing any plausible excuse to avoid physical contact,' Paul retorted mercilessly. 'Do you take me for a fool?'

No, he was far too astute, too worldly-wise to be foiled by such a trick, and she struggled desperately in vain to free her hands. 'I hardly know you,' she cried. 'Won't you allow me time to get to know you better?'

'What would that achieve?' he countered, his eyes darkening fractionally as they rested on her firm superbly shaped breasts. 'Can you perceive it will be any easier tomorrow or the day after, than now?'

Stacey glared at him, dislike evident in her expressive features. 'You're a brute,' she accused hatefully. 'An uncaring, insensitive *devil*!'

With his free hand Paul leaned out and turned off the water. 'I can be all those, and more,' he evinced brusquely. 'Continue to thwart me, and it will be to your disadvantage.' He collected two towels and tossed one towards her, his expression grim and forbidding. 'I have neither the inclination nor the intention to play games.'

Quickly enveloping her body with the large fluffy towel, she surreptitiously dried herself, then wound the towel sarong-wise round her slim curves.

'Have you finished?'

At the faintly mocking query she lifted her chin and glared defiantly as she swung round to face him. Anger lent her eyes a fiery sparkle, and she curbed her wayward tongue with difficulty as she preceded him through to the bedroom.

Crossing to the dressing-table, Stacey searched for a brush to restore order to her damp tousled hair. In the mirror she scarcely recognised the stormy features as her own, and she dragged the brush through the length of her hair with painful disregard for her scalp.

When she turned she saw that the counterpane had been discarded and placed on an ottoman at the foot of the bed, and her eyes widened at the manner in which the blankets had been tossed aside.

'Come here.' It was a command she had no intention of heeding, and she met his eyes defiantly. With a towel wrapped round his hips he looked vaguely satanical, and in that moment she was made shockingly aware of his intention to possess her—with or without her consent.

'I'm not afraid of you.' Fool, she cursed silently, you're scared stiff!

'You should be,' Paul declared harshly. 'I have a devilish temper when roused, and my patience is almost exhausted.'

'And like a docile little lamb I should lie down and accept the inevitable? Sorry, Mr Leandros—if you want me, you're going to have to come and get me!'

The expression in his eyes brought a silent scream to her throat, and without conscious thought she turned and ran—uncaring where she escaped to as long as it was away from the brutish man she hated with a violence that rocked her very being.

She hadn't taken more that three steps before hard hands caught hold of her shoulders, halting her flight. Then she was clawing him, hitting, scratching—on any part of his anatomy she could reach. Like a demented animal she fought against him, gasping with rage as he caught first one hand, then the other, behind her back.

Not content, she lashed out with her foot and gave an anguished cry as he yanked her hard against him.

'Stop it, you little wildcat!' He hardly seemed to feel the exertion her struggles had caused, yet she was breathing as if she had just run a mile.

'Oh, go to *hell*!'

With an angry oath he pulled the towel from around her body and tossed it aside, then he lowered his head to crush her lips, uncaring that he ground the delicate inner tissue against her teeth, yet still she refused to part her mouth and allow him entrance.

A stinging slap on her derrière brought an involuntary gasp, and then his mouth was on hers, firm and probing, his lips sensually hard as his mouth plundered hers in a kiss that destroyed every last illusion.

Not content, his hands roved over her slim body, teasing taut curves, probing intimately until she groaned out loud, then his lips began a slow exploratory descent, seducing with provocative expertise until against her will she felt the flame of awakening desire heat her limbs, encompassing her entire body so that she ached for fulfilment.

Hardly aware that her feet no longer touched the floor, she clung to the only solid entity in that emotional whirlpool until the silken warmth of the electrically-heated bed against her back brought a momentary return to sanity, and she began to struggle against Paul's lowered weight, striving to shift from beneath him.

'Let me go!' The cry left her throat as a desperate plea, but she was no match against his strength, and her agonised scream emerged as a silent moan against his mouth. Then he was still, and the lips that had wreaked such havoc with her soft mouth gentled and took on a seducing quality.

As the pain subsided he began to move, quieting her ineffectual struggles much as one would gentle a frightened child, until she was lulled into a sense of false security and she began to relax. Then it began— a slow tide that swelled into an explosion of sensual pleasure, leaving her gasping as the aftermath of ecstasy shook her body, and her mind reeled that a man she hated so much could be capable of arousing such feeling.

She must have drifted into sleep, for she woke to the sound of drapes being drawn, and she blinked against the light, unaware for a few heartstopping seconds of her whereabouts. Then it all came flooding back with frightening clarity, and it was all she could do not to bury her head in the pillow. As it was she slid upright into a sitting position with one hand clutching the sheet so that it covered her nakedness.

'Good morning. I hope you slept well?'

Stacey met the faint smile of the slim matron whom Paul had introduced the previous evening as his housekeeper, and took the breakfast tray rather gingerly, letting it rest on her lap. 'Thanks, Sophie—yes,' she managed politely, eyeing the tray with interest. She was hungry, and in need of the steaming hot coffee that teased her nostrils with its aroma.

'Mr Leandros regrets he will be unable to take lunch with you, and requests you to be ready at seven, as he has accepted an invitation to dine with friends.'

Has he indeed? Stacey pondered dubiously. Aloud, she acquiesced, adding her thanks for the breakfast tray, then watched idly as Sophie retreated from the room.

Memories from the previous night were startlingly vivid, and she attacked the light fluffy omelette with more than necessary force. Damn Paul Leandros! He was a brute, a formidable beast for forcing her to accept his lovemaking. She was stiff and sore, and had undoubtedly suffered several bruises beneath his hurtful hands. It certainly felt like it, she grimaced ruefully.

After helping herself to a second cup of coffee, she slipped out from between the sheets and slid her arms into a wrap, then she went into the bathroom and turned on the taps, adding a liberal quantity of bath essence.

Soaking unrepentantly in the hot scented water, Stacey ruminated on how she would spend the day. Exploring the double-storied mansion and surrounding grounds would take care of the morning, and in the afternoon she would visit the flat. Trisha probably wouldn't be home, but there she could think clearly without being constantly reminded of her hateful husband. If only she could defy him and refuse to accompany him tonight! He was far too arrogant, commanding her presence without so much as asking if she would like to go.

A slight smile curved her wide mouth. If she wasn't here, Paul would have to go alone, and the resultant gossip that would evolve from her absence would undoubtedly cause him embarrassment. And that was her sole aim—to hurt and humiliate him. Nothing would give her more pleasure.

Having completed her toilette, Stacey dressed in a burgundy woollen skirt and a cream jumper, then slipped her feet into knee-length suede boots. Her make-up was kept to a minimum, and she descended the stairs to the lower floor with the intention of acquainting herself with her new home.

The house was a large one, elegantly furnished with excellent taste in muted shades of cream and sage green, the plain walls adorned with expensive prints which provided necessary splashes of contrasting colour. Persian rugs covered the sage-green carpet at regularly spaced intervals in the lounge and dining-room, and towards the rear of the house there was a large family room, designed, she suspected, for Nicos' benefit, for it contained expensive electronic equipment, a billiards table, bookshelves that ran floor-to-ceiling and filled with a variety of first editions. Sliding glass doors opened out on to a paved patio, beyond which was a large swimming pool. As well as the large formal dining-room there was a smaller dining-room obviously intended for family use, and on the same floor there was a study which Stacey merely glanced into before closing the door. The upper floor comprised no fewer than six bedrooms and three bathrooms, and in the grounds adjoining the double garage was a complex where Sophie and her husband Alex resided. Altogether it bespoke a wealthy man's indulgence to his own comfort.

After a light lunch of tasty vegetable soup and fresh crusty rolls, Stacey donned a warm suede coat, collected her shoulder bag, then summoned a taxi, issuing a smiling but deliberately vague message to Sophie as to her intended whereabouts and proposed return.

The flat in Essendon was more or less as she had left it the previous morning, and with a sigh she set about restoring order, putting the washing machine in motion, then tidying the dishes stacked in the sink. Trisha was no help when it came to housework, and it remained to be seen if she would display an interest now that Stacey was no longer there.

The afternoon fled, and it was after four when she folded the ironing board and put away all the clothes. A much needed cup of coffee, then she would prepare a meal, utilising the oven for a casserole which Trisha could reheat. For herself she settled with steak and a salad, and she had just sat down at the table with her plate when the phone rang.

Stacey flew to answer it, then stood with her hand poised over the receiver. It couldn't be Trisha—she would hardly ring an empty flat, and if it was one of her friends, it wouldn't matter as Trisha wasn't here A quick glance at her watch revealed it to be six-thirty, and Stacey retreated, letting the insistent peal remain unanswered. There was a slim chance it might be Paul checking her whereabouts, and the last thing she wanted was for him to discover where she was. That would spoil everything. His anger she could face at a later hour.

She was in the kitchen tidying the dishes after having finished her solitary meal when the doorbell rang. A faint frown creased her forehead as she dried her hands on a nearby tea-towel and hastened to answer it.

Quite who she expected to find on the doorstep she wasn't sure, but certainly not the tall powerful figure of her husband.

'Paul!' His name shot from her lips involuntarily, and it took only seconds to register that he was furiously angry.

'I presume this to be one of your devious schemes?' he drawled grimly, and a blush slowly tinged her cheeks a delicate pink.

'Why?' she demanded baldly. 'Did you imagine I'd left you?'

'No. You may hate me,' he drawled silkily, 'but you love your sister too much to negate our—arrangement.'

'Two *years*!' Stacey flung wildly. 'I must have been out of my mind!'

A muscle tautened palpably along the edge of his jaw, and his eyes hardened until they resembled jet flints. 'I warned you *once* not to trifle with my temper,' he uttered harshly. 'Don't try me too far, Stacey. You won't like the consequences.'

'Oh, dear,' she mocked, gazing up at him guilelessly. 'Am I to be punished, Paul?' She ignored the steely glint in those ebony eyes. 'Will you curtail my allowance—or have you something more diabolical in mind?'

For a terrible moment she thought he was going to hit her, then he stepped inside and slammed the door. 'You have ten minutes in which to change and make yourself presentable. We're already late.'

'I'm not going with you.'

'Oh yes, you are,' Paul insisted brusquely. 'Go and get changed—quickly.'

'I won't!' she refused with thinly veiled fury. 'Anyway,' she added with some satisfaction, 'I haven't got any clothes here suitable to wear.'

He thrust an overnight bag down on to a nearby chair, then fixed her with a look of such inflexible implacability that had she not been so angry she would have subsided into a quivering jelly. Attired in a dark evening suit over which he had added an elegant impeccably cut coat, he exuded leashed power and a sophistication she had not previously encountered. It was madness to goad him, but some inner imp led her on and she was powerless to desist.

'There's a dress in there, and shoes,' he told her. 'Get changed while I make a phone call.' His searing glance made a mockery of her defiance, yet still she refused to obey him.

'I've no intention of coming with you.'

If it were possible his expression became even more forbidding, and she felt the beginnings of fear as he thrust her before him into one of the two bedrooms the flat possessed. 'You have a choice,' he snarled savagely. 'Change your clothes on your own accord—or I'll do it for you.'

'Like hell you will!'

'How do you propose to stop me?' With barely controlled violence he yanked her towards him, then caught hold of her jumper and swept it over her head.

'What do you think you're doing?' Stacey gasped as his hands sought the zip fastening of her skirt.

'You just ran out of time, Stacey,' he averred ruthlessly, resisting her attempts to prevent him removing her outer clothing. With humiliating strength he held her immobile while he slipped the dress over her head and fastened the zip, then he pushed her towards the mirror. 'Your hair—brush it,' he commanded, and she turned on him with furiously sparkling eyes.

'You're unspeakable, do you know that? Oh, I could —oh——'

'Lost for words, my dear wife?' he taunted, and without thinking her hand flew to his face.

The ensuing silence almost made her scream, then with cruel deliberation he kissed her—a single hard kiss that brought tears to her eyes, and she tasted blood where he had heartlessly ground the inner tissue against her teeth.

'I warned you never to do that again,' Paul told her bleakly, and his eyes raked mercilessly over her features. 'Do something to your face,' he instructed bluntly. 'I'll phone our hostess and explain that we've been unavoidably detained.'

Stacey watched his retreating back until it was out of sight down the hallway, then she took a deep steadying breath. Her hands shook—in fact, she felt as if she was shaking all over. Dear God, such anger! Never before had any man had the power to drive her emotions into such a state of turmoil. How could she dine in his company among other guests and contrive to act as if everything was normal between them— even effect a fondness for him? As it was she had brought retribution upon her head. Dared she risk angering him further?

Shakily she took up a brush and attempted to restore some order to her hair, then made use of Trisha's make-up. Although nothing could hide the suspicious brightness of her eyes, or the faint tightening at the edges of her mouth. By the time Paul entered the room again she was ready, albeit reluctantly.

The swift encompassing glance he spared her did little to bolster her morale, and without a word she preceded him from the room and made her way out to the car. He had gained a victory—and she experienced the bitter feeling that it was only the first of many.

Somehow she managed to get through the evening, proffering polite conversation liberally dispersed with several smiles, and it was to her credit that she accorded Paul a measure of seeming affection that was almost a match for his. It was doubtful there was one guest present who didn't think they presented a loving couple, and maintaining the façade sapped all her reserves of strength. Even so, she was unable to resist a little subtle sarcasm on occasion, and her deliberate adoration brought more than one chilling glance upon her unrepentant head.

When it came time to leave she could only view their departure with a mixture of relief mingled with fearful fascination for the retribution she knew must inevitably follow.

In the car she remained silent, having nothing whatever to say, and she entered the house wearily, feeling utterly enervated.

'Goodnight.' Stacey murmured the words with polite neutrality and made to cross the foyer to the curved staircase.

'Not yet, I think,' Paul drawled with hateful sarcasm, and she turned wearily to face him.

'All right, Paul, let's get it over and done with.'

'So brave!' he derided softly, his eyes hard and darkly forbidding. 'Never has any women moved me to such a degree of anger. It is as much as I can do to keep my hands off you!'

Her face paled slightly. 'You wouldn't dare!'

'No?' His mouth twisted with cynical humour, and she spluttered into indignant speech.

'If you so much as lay a hand on me, I—I'll never speak to you again!'

One eyebrow arched sardonically. 'I quake at the very thought.'

'Oh, go to hell!' she thrust belligerently, and moved to pass him.

A hand on her arm brought her to an abrupt halt. 'Be careful you don't join me there,' Paul warned formidably, and she lifted her chin defiantly.

'What makes you think I haven't already arrived?'

The instant before he moved she knew she had gone too far, but by then it was too late, and her startled cry held stark fear as Paul hefted her across one shoulder and made for the stairs.

'Put me down, you fiend!' She beat angry fists against his powerful back, struggling as much as her undignified posture would allow, but it was to no avail, and as he entered their bedroom there were very real tears clouding her vision.

The door snapped shut, aided by a backward kick from his foot, then he strode into the centre of the room, uncaring of the blows raining down his back.

'You're unspeakable, do you know that?' Stacey cried in temper. 'Put me down at once, or I'll scream!'

Without a word he slipped off each of her shoes in turn, then threw them to the floor. Next, he slid her down to stand in front of him and proceeded to take off her coat, evading with effortless ease any attempt she made to stop him. Then came the dress, quickly followed by her slip.

'What are you doing?' Stacey gasped, her breathing rapid from so much fruitless exertion.

'I would imagine it is quite evident what I intend to do,' Paul returned implacably, and with a quick thrust he twisted her across one powerful thigh.

The slaps he administered were mercilessly hard and stung long after he set her upright.

'A few more bruises,' he drawled hatefully. 'You seem to have a penchant for collecting them.'

'I hate you!' Stacey choked. 'I've never hated anyone or anything as much in my entire life!'

His eyes hardened considerably as he raked her stormy features, then he reached out and hauled her into his arms. 'In that case, I have nothing to lose.'

She had to clench her teeth in a effort to still her trembling lips, and the look she cast him held mutinous antipathy. 'I loathe having you touch me,' she maintained shakily. 'The only consolation I have is that each occasion lessens the debt I owe.'

'I could strangle you with my bare hands,' Paul threatened inimically. 'Yet entwined with that is the desire to make love to you until you scream for mercy.'

'Love?' Stacey derided. '*Love?* Last night was *hell*!'

His steady contemplation was unnerving. 'The circumstances weren't exactly conducive to gentle possession,' he informed her dryly. 'Had I know you were—untouched, I would have ensured that you suffered less. Tonight will be different.'

'I doubt it!'

'You disbelieve me?' he taunted, and her eyes lit with bitter enmity.

'I intend fighting you every inch of the way,' she vowed.

'Can't you perceive there may come a time when you may not want to?'

'You have an outsize ego,' she accused trenchantly,

and his faint smile held a tinge of mocking amusement.

'No—just an all-encompassing knowledge of women.'

'I don't doubt your experience,' Stacey denied witheringly.

'Yet from your limited knowledge you presume to judge.'

She was suddenly weary, inexplicably tired of doing both physical and verbal battle. As determined as she was not to be held beneath Paul Leandros' tyrannical thumb, asserting her independence was proving to be no easy task. Two years yawned ahead like a long dark tunnel from which she could see no visible light, and the mere thought of remaining with such a man was fraught with emotions so volatile that retaining her sanity was going to demand every ounce of strength she possessed.

'I'm tired,' she said at last, conscious that his hands on her arms no longer bruised her flesh. 'I'd like to go to bed.'

Hard fingers trailed over her shoulders to the back fastening of her bra and deftly unclasped it.

'Don't! I'm quite capable of doing that,' she flung, and glimpsed the way his mouth twisted with cynical humour.

'I was merely giving assistance.'

'Oh—why not?' she capitulated hatefully. 'You've already removed most of my clothing—you may as well finish the task!'

'Why make it so difficult for yourself?' Paul demanded softly, his voice lowered to little more than a husky murmur.

'It *is* difficult—you must know that!' Stacey choked resentfully as his head lowered, and there was little she could do to escape those frankly sensuous lips as they covered hers.

'Relax, child,' he bade. 'Open your mouth.'

She gave a slight negative shake of her head, then gasped involuntarily as his teeth teased back her lower lip, partially drawing it into his mouth and providing just sufficient pressure so that she daren't pull back.

Then he drew her body close so that her breasts touched the roughened texture of his jacket, and the sensitive nipples hardened and began to pulsate with the delicate friction. Her eyes searched his, unconsiously begging him to desist, but a flame leapt in answer, and there was no doubting his physical arousal.

Slowly he began to discard his clothes until there were no restricting garments between them, and her face flooded with mortifying colour as his hands began a leisurely intimate exploration, then his mouth was on hers, hard and insistently demanding, forcing entry to the sweet moistness her lips protected, and she gave an inaudible groan of despair. Yet still he chose not to afford any release from the aching emotion he aroused, and she began to moan softly as it became almost unbearable.

'Please, Paul—*please*,' she begged, straining away from him in an effort to escape the erotic ecstasy his mouth evoked as it trailed at will over her body.

Not content, he sought her breasts and each vulnerable nipple, teasing first one and then the other into a pulsating culmination of exquisite pain so that she cried out with it and dragged his head away.

'Please—no more. Oh God!' she sobbed quietly, and her whole body shook as his mouth fastened on hers with unerring possession.

What happened afterwards took on a dreamlike

quality, and she had scant recollection of the vibrantly-alive being she became beneath Paul's sensual mastery, and was unable to reconcile the sensations he aroused as being anything related to the hatred she professed to feel for him.

CHAPTER THREE

SUNDAY brought a slight improvement in the weather, and after a leisurely breakfast Paul relayed the information that they were to lunch with his mother prior to taking Nicos to participate in a sporting fixture during the afternoon, after which they would dine together before returning Nicos to boarding school.

'I trust you can be relied upon not to resort to any childish displays of temper?'

Stacey returned her empty cup down on to its saucer and regarded him carefully. Looking at him brought back memories she would prefer to forget, and the knowledge that he could entice from her a physical response brought a faint tinge of pink to her cheeks. She couldn't help but wonder how he could sit there so calmly, when only hours before...

'You want to maintain a pretence for the benefit of your family?' she parried coolly.

'My son never knew his mother,' Paul revealed inscrutably. 'Already, after one brief meeting, it has been evident you both share a natural empathy. Whatever reason I have chosen to make you my wife, I insist Nicos remains unaware of it.'

'I am to appear to be a loving wife—and mother?'

'Nicos is my son,' he told her quietly. 'I'll do anything in my power to protect him.'

'What of the succession of women in your life? Have you been able to protect him from them?'

His eyes glinted dangerously. 'My private affairs remained precisely that—private.'

'Remarkably easy, with Nicos safely ensconsed in boarding school,' she condemned.

'By the living Christ, you have a vicious tongue,' he swore emotively, and she retaliated swiftly:

'You continually bring out the worst in me! I won't be subservient, in fear and trembling of your irascible temper. I accept marriage to you as the price I have to pay—but don't expect a willing, sacrificial *lamb*!'

His eyes bored relentlessly into hers for an unending length of time, then he drawled with dangerous softness, 'If it's a battle you want, then that is what you will get—with no holds barred.'

Stacey stood to her feet, momentarily feeling at an advantage as she looked down at him. 'I never expected it to be otherwise.'

Paul rose from the table, and his height was intimidating. 'We leave at eleven. Until then, I'll be in the study.'

Without a word Stacey turned and left the room, crossing the hallway to the foyer, then mounting the stairs to the bedroom. There was a phone beside the bed, and she had a desperate need to hear a familiar voice.

With faintly shaking fingers she dialled the numerous digits, then waited with scant patience for Trisha to answer.

After a seemingly interminable length of time the receiver was lifted, and a cross sleep-heavy voice barked an ill-manned greeting.

'Trisha, were you still in bed?' Stacey queried apologetically.

'Where else would you expect me to be at this ungodly hour?'

'It's almost nine o'clock,' Stacey reasoned, and Trisha gave an impatient sigh.

'What's so urgent you have to ring me this early in the morning—or are you just checking that I'm home?'

She swallowed the lump in her throat with difficulty. 'No,' she denied slowly, hating the dissension that always seemed to be evident between them these days. 'I just wanted to find out if you were okay.'

'Well, I'm fine,' came the swift reply. 'Now, can I go back to sleep?'

'You're managing all right in the flat on your own?' Stacey queried quickly. 'There're no problems?'

'Not a one, sister dear. If there was, I'd contact you, never fear!' Her voice rose a fraction. 'Now, for God's sake, is that all? I'm freezing cold standing here in the hallway!'

'Yes,' Stacey responded, 'that's all. I'll ring you again in a few days, and we'll meet for lunch.'

'Sure. Now, goodbye.'

At the sound of the receiver clunking down in her ear a single disconsolate tear spilled over and ran slowly down her cheek, and she brushed it away with an angry movement. Feeling sorry for herself wouldn't do the slightest bit of good; she had to do something constructive.

Despite having had an early morning shower, she elected to have another and wash her hair, then by the time she had blow-dried it she could dress and apply her make-up. Should there be any time in hand, there was an enviable collection of cassettes in the downstairs family room among which she would surely find something that would soothe her fractured nerves.

At exactly five to eleven Paul entered the room, his expression enigmatic at the sight of Stacey leaning against the sliding glass door seemingly intent on the wind gusting leaves on the lawn outside.

'If you're ready, we'll get away. Dress warmly,' he advised. 'The park is bound to be cold.'

Stacey turned slowly to face him. 'Park?' she queried, clearly puzzled.

'Nicos is playing soccer this afternoon, remember?' he reminded her sardonically, and she lowered her head against his biting cynicism.

'Yes, of course.' She drew level with him, coming to an abrupt halt as he grasped her arm.

'I have your word that you'll behave yourself this afternoon?'

Stacey lifted her chin and directed a particularly scathing glance at his tautly-chiselled broad-boned features. 'I'll adopt an exemplary manner,' she acceded stiffly, adding, 'For Nicos' sake.'

Paul accepted it silently, dropping his hand and allowing her to pass.

'I'll get my coat.'

A sleek BMW saloon was parked outside the main entrance, and Stacey slid into the passenger seat to have Paul close her door before moving round to slip in behind the wheel.

'Where does your mother live?' The query was voiced more out of curiosity than a desire to make conversation.

'Frankston, overlooking the bay.' He swung the powerful vehicle on to the main road and headed it towards the motorway south.

'Will anyone else be there?'

'No.'

Stacey sat silently surveying the passing scenery for the time it took to reach the attractive seaside suburb, and she gave an inaudible sigh of relief when the car slowed and turned into a long curving driveway.

The house was an imposing split-level, combining a pleasing mixture of roughed brick and cream-painted timber, the windows multi-paned with dark brown shutters.

Almost as soon as the car drew to a halt, the front door opened and a casually attired Nicos came down the steps to greet them.

'Dad—Stacey! How are you?' He opened the car door for Stacey to alight, and her smile was genuinely warm as she thanked him.

'Let's get inside, shall we?' Paul suggested, placing a hand on his son's shoulder, and Nicos made a laughing reference to the inclement weather as he walked beside Stacey and his father to the front door.

Mrs Leandros—senior—Stacey amended with a mental grimace, was a well-proportioned woman in her late sixties, vaguely forbidding in appearance and possessing a natural dignity that bordered on hauteur. Stacey was inclined to add—typically Greek. But that would have been presumtuous, as the only other Greek she knew was her husband, and her association with him hardly made her an authority.

Lunch was surprisingly formal, and Stacey had to concede that if it wasn't for Nicos' presence she would have become submerged beneath an almost anachronistic protocol totally alien to her.

'You are several years younger than my son, are you not?'

Oh dear, she thought wryly, here it comes—the third degree! 'I'm twenty-three, Mrs Leandros,' she revealed quietly.

'You look younger.' With the air of a matriarch, Paul's mother conferred what was obviously intended as a great honour. 'Paul calls me Mama—so must you.'

'Thank you,' Stacey acknowledged with equal politeness.

'You were employed in a hospital, I believe?'

'Yes—as a physiotherapist.'

'Your friendship with my son has been a long-standing one? Until Thursday of last week, we, his family, had heard no mention of you.'

With deliberate intent Paul reached out and entwined his fingers in hers, then cast Stacey a look of such infinite warmth she had to blink rather rapidly. 'It is enough that Stacey is my wife, and as such I must insist you refrain from subjecting her to this examination.'

'Is it not acceptable for me to want to know more about my daughter-in-law?'

'I suggest you direct your questions to me,' Paul stated firmly.

'I am merely concerned for your happiness, and that of Nicos,' Mrs Leandros said stiffly, and Paul laughed, his eyes gleaming with ill-concealed humour.

'Mama, you are curious. Admit it!'

'So? Am I not entitled to be?' The query was imperiously delivered. 'You have escorted several women to various functions, maintained a fleeting relationship with many—yet always in the background has been Christina Goulandris. It is she I thought you would ultimately marry.'

'Grandma, you are embarrassing Stacey.' The reprimand came surprisingly from Nicos, and Stacey longed to assure him she was far from embarrassed!

'Nicos, you would challenge me?' Mrs Leandros' expression was incredulous and more than a little scandalous as she turned to her son. 'Paul?'

'Stacey has already established an affection with

Nicos,' Paul drawled. 'He considers it his privilege to defend hear.'

'Really? And his rudeness to me is of little consequence?'

Sensing a storm brewing, Stacey quickly sought to avert it. 'This moussaka is excellent,' she complimented. 'I haven't tasted anything like it before. It is your own recipe?'

The frankly sardonic gleam in Paul's eyes as he glanced in her direction brought a defiant tightening of her lips, and she refrained from uttering so much as a word for the remainder of the meal.

It was two o'clock when they slid into the car and drove north from Frankston, heading back towards the city. Conversation was confined mainly between father and son except when Nicos sought to include Stacey, and there was grim warning in the look Paul shot her the instant Nicos collected his sports holdall and disappeared towards the changing room.

'You are scarcely an avid conversationalist,' he commented brusquely, his brooding gaze following his son's rapidly disappearing figure.

'I talked to Nicos,' she retorted swiftly, and a muscle leapt along his jaw.

'Exactly. But not at all to me,' he declared bluntly, lifting one expressive eyebrow. 'Surely that would seem a little—strange, from such a newly-married woman?'

'I see,' Stacey expelled with heavy sarcasm. 'I'm to appear head-over-heels in love with you—besotted, in fact.' She moved forward and deliberately slipped her arm through his. 'If I cling on to you and gaze adoringly into your eyes, will that please you?'

'Careful!' Paul warned dangerously, and she laughed up at him, pouting her lips with studied provocativeness.

'Why, darling, what can you possibly do in front of so many people?'

Without a word he took hold of her shoulder and turned her towards him, enfolding her close as he bent his head. His mouth was punishingly brutal, bruising the soft tissue until she thought the skin must split, then with an inaudible growl of disgust he lifted his head to gaze down at her through narrowed lids.

'When will you learn not to provoke me?'

'I hate you,' Stacey managed through painful lips. 'But most of all, I hate being used.'

'Then continue to hate me,' he said hardily. 'At least it's an honest emotion.'

'The *only* emotion you'll ever arouse in me,' she assured with quiet vehemence.

'Nicos is on the field,' Paul directed. 'We will stand on the sideline and watch.'

Stacey moved forward with him, prompted by the arm around her waist and the steel-like grasp on her arm. More than anything she wanted to wrench away and hurl bitter invective to release some of the built-up fury that raged inside her, but Nicos' presence as well as that of others near by forestalled her.

For fifteen minutes Stacey watched the game progress in total silence, then the pain from Paul's excruciating grip forced her into speech.

'You're hurting me!' she gasped through tight lips, and with an impatient oath he relinquished her arm.

After half-time Stacey ignored the powerful man beside her and entered into the spirit of the game by cheering Nicos and his team to victory, and even went so far as to give him a congratulatory hug as he joined them after the game refreshed by a shower and change of clothes.

Enthusiastic at the outcome, Nicos suggested they

visit a nearby bistro with other members of the team to celebrate, and this they did, joining in the revelry that evolved over the ensuing hour.

Stacey began to dread dinner with just Paul and Nicos for company. Maintaining an amicable front in Nicos' presence was going to be no mean acting feat, and suddenly she wanted the evening over and done with. At least alone with Paul she could resort to their usual state of animosity.

Shortly after six o'clock they left for a charmingly intimate restaurant where the cuisine was wholly Greek, and Stacey deferred the choice entirely to Paul, adding with seeming sweetness:

'Darling, I may have married a Greek, but I know nothing whatever about your traditional dishes. I have no dislikes with regard to food,' she paused deliberately and offered him a singularly sweet smile. 'You choose something you think will please me.'

The look Paul directed her promised retaliation and she let her eyes widen guilelessly as he gave their order.

For the entire meal Stacey gave Nicos her undivided attention, engaging him in conversation with the genuine attempt to develop the friendship that was already growing between them. He was an uncomplicated young man, direct and thoroughly likeable—in total antithesis of his father.

At precisely seven-thirty Paul escorted them to the car, and drove the short distance to Nicos' boarding school, depositing him outside his chosen dormitory before sweeping down the long drive and into the main stream of traffic.

It was now that Stacey felt vulnerable, tired and contrarily at odds emotionally. More than anything she would have liked to entreat Paul to take her home so that she could take a leisurely bath and then slip into bed. But to go back to that two-storied edifice would only serve to hasten a confrontation with her indomitable husband, and she was reluctant to face him and endure his lovemaking. On the spur of the moment she found herself saying:

'Could we call round to the flat—Trisha's flat? I left a few things there that I'd like to collect,' she invented wildly, conscious of the lightning glance Paul cast her.

'You don't want to return home yet, is that it?' he queried with drawling cynicism. 'What are you afraid of?'

'Nothing,' she returned with biting sarcasm. 'I'm still responsible for my sister, and I'd like to see her. Do you mind?'

'I imagine Trisha is managing very well without you,' Paul averred brusquely, swinging the wheel as the opulent car took a curve, then easing it to a halt before a set of traffic lights.

'You won't take me?'

His shrug was slight and almost undetectable in the darkness. 'If that is what you want.'

A line of cars of various description lined the drive, and music reverberated with muted sound as they mounted the steps to the front door.

'A party?' Paul slanted sardonically, and Stacey pursed her lips in silent antipathy.

The door was opened after several minutes by a garishly-attired female who promptly pulled them inside with a wide grin, then waved a long cigarette-holder in the general direction of the lounge.

'Through there, darlings. You have been invited, I presume?'

'I'm Trisha's sister,' Stacey said clearly, her voice rising to be heard above the music.

'Oh well, that's all right, then,' the other laughed. 'Grab a drink—there's beer, gin and wine. If you want anything else, you should have brought it yourself.'

The usually immaculate lounge was almost unrecognisable from the number of bodies draped everywhere. Couples were on their feet dancing, moving in time to the music, while others alternatively sat or lay stretched out on the floor. The air was thick with tobacco smoke and the smell of liquor, and it was evident the party had been going for several hours despite the fact that it was little more than eight o'clock.

Stacey searched through the gloom and discerned Trisha in the arms of a young man, and her cheeks grew hot at the manner in which they were behaving. She wanted to switch on the light, evict everyone, and set the room to order—then demand an explanation. But she did none of these things; instead, she turned to Paul and said a trifle desperately:

'I'll just have a few words with Trisha, then we'll go.'

Paul's eyes were hooded, his expression unfathomable as he gave the briefest of nods, and Stacey left his side and began weaving her way to the corner of the room.

Trisha's surprise wasn't feigned, and Stacey preferred to forget the manner in which her sister greeted her. Rather than create a scene she simply turned and moved back to where Paul stood, and she scarcely paused before making her way to the front door.

It had all been too much—the constant battles with her inimicable husband, the equally inimicable woman who was his mother, and now this. She wanted to curl up into a ball and die.

The drive back to Kew was conducted in total silence, and as soon as they gained the front entrance into the foyer Stacey made for the stairs.

A hand on her arm forestalled her, and she looked askance of the inscrutable man less than a foot away.

'A drink, Stacey,' Paul indicated quietly, but she pulled away, her eyes sparking furiously alive as he didn't lessen his grasp. 'Come—I insist.'

She gave an angry wrench. 'You can insist all you like. I don't want one.'

'Not even something almost totally innocuous?'

'No! Now, will you leave me alone!' She was almost shouting, and stupid angry tears hurt the back of her eyes.

'Go to bed,' Paul directed bluntly. 'You are in need of a good night's rest.'

Bitterness rose like gall in her throat. 'There's not much chance of that, is there?'

His eyelids lowered slightly. 'I am not totally insensitive.'

'You could have fooled me! In the space of forty-eight hours I've been raped, beaten, subjected to all kinds of licentious behaviour, berated for marrying you. God!' she uttered piously. 'If only your mother knew how much I loathed you, she might rest easy. Christina whatever-her-name-is is welcome to you—believe me, two years can't pass quickly enough!'

Without a word Paul swept her into his arms, hefting her wildly struggling form over one shoulder as he strode to the stairs, mounting them and making his way to the bedroom with effortless ease.

Once inside he moved to the bed and dropped her down on to the brocade counterpane. 'You have three minutes to undress without my help. I wouldn't advise you to waste any of it.'

Stacey regarded him mutinously. 'I won't get changed if you're going to stand there and watch me.'

His laugh held cynical amusement. 'I'm familiar with every curve, or have you forgotten?'

'I loathe you,' she declared with calculating slowness. 'You're nothing less than a devil, and I hate every second I'm forced to spend in your company!'

'It's a long time before your release,' Paul stated implacably, and leaning forward he pulled her to her feet. 'Hate may change.'

'Never!' She twisted in vain to escape his hold, and when his hand went to the buttons on her blouse she lost the tenuous hold over her temper and lashed out at him, beating her fists against his chest, arms and shoulders like a demented cornered animal.

'Stop it!' The summons was curtly delivered as he caught hold of her flailing hands, easily stilling her attack, and she let out a moan that mingled anger with despair.

With a strangely gentle gesture Paul lifted a hand and pushed her tumbled hair back from her face, then let his fingers trail down to lift her chin. Touching her lips with an idle finger, he probed the lower lip downwards so that the soft tissue was exposed, and his eyes narrowed fractionally at the grazing evident.

'You fight like a little wildcat,' he offered ruminatively. 'It's only to be expected my temper be roused— the consequences of which haven't proved pleasant, have they?'

'I don't cower with fright at the mere thought of displeasing you,' Stacey owned shakily, and the inkling of a smile flickered across his strongly etched features.

'No,' he drawled. 'You have spirit, I grant you— perhaps a shade too much for your own good.'

'I'm honest in my association with others,' she stated

stoically. 'If I hate, I hate to the fullest measure.'

'So it would appear,' Paul acceded dryly. 'What of love, Stacey? Could any one man be certain of your unending devotion?'

'If he could prove he deserved it.'

'What would that involve?'

Stacey looked at him carefully. 'Love—fidelity.'

'Hm,' he pondered thoughtfully. 'It might be worth it at that.'

'You—faithful to one woman?' She gave a disbelieving laugh. 'Oh, come on! The way your mother tells it, you've know so many it would be impossible to settle with one. Poor Christina has been waiting for years!'

'If I had wanted to marry Christina, I would have done so,' Paul told her coolly.

'Instead, you married me,' she said slowly. 'When you could have insisted on something less binding, you chose marriage. Why, Paul?'

'It suited me,' he responded enigmatically, and she strained away from him.

'But I'm involved, too,' she cried emotively. 'I have feelings—I'm not a puppet you can manipulate at will!'

'Your affection for Trisha was the reason you accepted my proposal—the alternative was untenable, isn't that true?'

She lifted stormy eyes to his, hating him. 'And now I must make another payment against my outstanding debt,' she snapped trenchantly.

'Poor little girl,' Paul drawled hatefully, drawing her close. 'You possess a delightfully responsive body. Careful you don't begin to enjoy it—to do so would be disastrous, wouldn't it?' he mocked, gazing down at her with darkening eyes.

Stacey felt a strange tremor shake her slim form at

his taunting words, and as his lips descended to brush her cheek she experienced a shaft of acute physical pleasure that exploded in seemingly slow motion until her stomach and lower limbs were encompassed by it.

She gave an inaudible groan as his hands loosened her blouse and discarded it, and her breasts grew heavy with an indescribable ache as he began to caress them.

Slowly, with suitably adept movements and without seeming to do so, Paul removed every last vestige of clothing, and Stacey gave a startled cry when she felt his nakedness against her own.

His mouth, warm and persuasive, dispelled any further protest, and after a while she ceased to think clearly as he exerted undoubted sensual mastery in bringing alive emotions she never dreamed existed. Then she was lost, swept upwards in a storm of sensual feeling so that she cried out with it, and she had little recollection of the way she clung to him, responding in a manner which brought forth an exultant growl deep in Paul's throat.

Afterwards she fell asleep in his arms, curled into the curve of his body, and the restless state in which she spent the night attested to the silent conflict of her unconscious mind.

CHAPTER FOUR

'I'M going into the city today,' Stacey announced baldly as she sat down opposite Paul at the breakfast table on Tuesday morning. Every attempt she had made to contact Trisha the previous day had proved fruitless.

Paul regarded her thoughtfully over the top of his newspaper. 'Any particular reason for doing so?'

'Why?' she bristled defensively. 'Have you any objection?'

'What would you do if I said yes?' he countered sardonically.

'Go just the same.' Determination lent her eyes an angry sparkle.

One eyebrow rose slightly as he mocked, 'Even knowing that to thwart me will bring retribution?'

She lifted her chin fractionally. 'What can you do to me, Paul?' Her gaze was startling direct. 'About the only thing left is to lock me indoors, and I don't believe you're that feudal.'

'Stacey,' he warned softly, 'I have no desire to trade insults so early in the day. Go into the city by all means. Alex will drive you.'

'He won't,' she denied emphatically. 'I have my own car, remember?'

Paul shrugged negligibly. 'As you wish. We are dining out this evening,' he informed her, sparing her a searching glance. 'Please ensure you are ready at six.'

'Where?'

His eyes hardened. 'Is it of any consequence? Or do you simply intend doing battle?'

'Clothes, Paul,' she enlightened him. 'I'm sure you'd prefer me to be correctly attired.'

'My mother is giving a formal dinner party,' he told her with a measure of cynicism, and her stomach did a rapid somersault.

'Hell!' she muttered inelegantly, her mind beginning to boggle at the prospect—worse, what she would wear.

'Not entirely,' Paul assured her mockingly. 'I will be there.'

Stacey gave a barely derisive snort. 'Your support will be most gratifying!'

'You are my wife,' he reminded her coldly. 'As such you are assured respect.'

'That cheers me no end.' Her agile imagination flew ahead, picturing what the evening would be like—the elegantly gowned women, self-assured and totally sophisticated in a manner that only wealth could provide. She would be the cynosure of all eyes, her every gesture discreetly watched. Nothing could be more ghastly.

'You have nothing suitable to wear, is that it?' He picked up his cup and drained the contents. 'Call into my office when you get into the city; I will have arranged for you to utilise my credit facilities.'

'I have my own money,' she said stoically.

'On second thoughts, I will re-shuffle my afternoon appointments,' Paul determined as he stood to his feet. 'Meet me at two in the office.'

'You'll come shopping with me?' Her voice rose in disbelief. 'Why? Don't you trust my judgment?'

'I doubt your bank account will run to original haute couture gowns,' he informed her cynically. 'I have some experience in such matters, and my presence will ensure suitable attention.'

'Is there anything you're not experienced in, Paul?' she parried sweetly. 'Or perhaps you'd better not answer that, on the grounds that an admission might incriminate you.'

'I shall have my revenge for that remark later,' he threatened silkily, and she gave a careless shrug.

'Go to work, Paul.' She was suddenly tired of bandying words with him, and she endeavoured not to look startled as he crossed round to her side. 'What do you want?'

'This.' He bent down, holding her head fast as he branded her mouth with his own in a kiss that was hatefully brutal.

'You devil!' Stacey accorded bitterly several seconds later, and his eyes glittered ominously.

'Eventually you must learn it is folly to provoke me.'

'I hope you burn in hell!' she delivered waspishly, running shaking fingers over her bruised lips. 'I'm not going anywhere with you this evening. The thought sickens me!'

Strong fingers bit painfully into the delicate bones of her shoulder. 'You will come. Be certain all hell will break loose if you don't.'

The threat wasn't an idle one, and she shivered in spite of herself. Paul Leandros was a force to be reckoned with, and she was a fool to tangle with him. Each battle, either verbal or physical, saw him steadily emerging as the victor. It would prove far less painful if she conceded defeat and accepted his superiority.

She raised rebellious eyes to his, hating him to the very depths of her being. 'I'll be there—if only not to give your mother the satisfaction of having me abstain.'

The look he gave her was hard and unfathomable, and after he had left the room Stacey slumped in her chair, totally enervated.

At precisely ten-thirty she parked her small car, locked it, then set out briskly for Elizabeth Street. It was bitterly cold, the wind fierce, and rain was imminent. For a moment she hesitated between slipping into a nearby coffee lounge for a reviving hot drink, then elected to enter Myers department store instead.

The throng of shoppers and the warmth of the heated store was welcoming, and for the next hour she browsed contentedly, adding a few purchases to her bag, then conscious of the time she slipped out on to the street and rode a tram up Bourke Street to the towering office block where Trisha worked.

Taking an elevator to the fifth floor, she waited in the corridor for the few remaining minutes until her sister was due to leave for lunch, and as soon as the door swung open she scanned the mingling heads for Trisha.

At last she sighted her, and the smile she summoned was faintly anxious. 'Hi,' she greeted warmly. 'I was in town and thought we might have lunch together.'

'Why not with Paul?' Trisha queried with a slight frown after offering a perfunctory greeting.

'I'm meeting him later,' Stacey dismissed. 'Where shall we go?'

'Somewhere expensive,' Trisha insisted firmly. 'You can afford it.'

It was on the tip of Stacey's tongue to demur, but instead she gave a slight shrug. 'Okay. There's a good Chinese restaurant not far from here.'

When they were seated Stacey waited until their order was taken before leaning forward. 'I've been trying to contact you since yesterday,' she said lightly, and Trisha made a slight moue.

'I've been busy. You know how it is.'

'Why don't you get one of your friends to come and

stay at the flat for a while?' Stacey suggested. 'I hate the thought of you being there alone.'

Trisha gave an expressive sigh. 'I know—I'm too young to take care of myself,' she mimicked sarcastically. 'The trouble with you is that you're trying too hard to be mother, father and sister all rolled into one. If you left me alone and didn't breathe down my neck at every opportunity we might get on a lot better.' She tossed back a wayward lock of long brown hair, then gazed at Stacey defiantly. 'I've got a good job, I can support myself. Okay, maybe now and then I get a little wild. Everyone does madcap things from time to time. Oh, *you* didn't, I know. You were only sixteen when Mum and Dad died, yet you managed. Well, I can too. Just don't try to be so protective. Half the time I do what I do just to spite you.'

Stacey took a deep breath. 'So—"don't call me, I'll call you", is that it? Dammit, Trisha, we're sisters! You're the only living relative I have in the world, bar a cousin or two twice removed, whose names I can't even remember! We should be close, but we're poles apart.'

'That's just it—we *are* different. Maybe I'm more like Dad than you, or vice versa—I don't know; I can't remember either parent very clearly. But, Stacey, you've got your life and I've got mine. Stop trying to live it for me, and let me get on with living it myself, *please*. All of a sudden I'm free, and believe me, I love it!'

'Well, just don't let it go to your head,' Stacey advised with a shaky smile.

'There you go again, in the role of admonishing parent. Try and see me as a fellow human for whom you have no responsibility whatsoever. Maybe we might even be friends.'

There was no time like the present. 'Well, *friend*,' she began with slight emphasis, 'you can advise me what to wear tonight. Paul and I are dining at his mother's home, together with several guests. Just how formal is "formal"?'

'Buy the most exclusive, expensive dress you can find,' Trisha declared swiftly. 'Leave your hair loose, take time and care with your make-up, wear one piece of expensive jewellery, and wear the most stunning pair of imported French shoes you can buy.' Her smile was wickedly gamin. 'I forgot perfume—Guerlain's Chamade is exactly you. Get some.' Her nose wrinkled expressively. 'Mrs Leandros is forbidding, isn't she?'

'Terrifying,' Stacey amended, adding silently—like mother, like son.

'Meet me for lunch on Friday and you can tell me all about it,' Trisha suggested, pulling the cuff back from her wrist and checking her watch. 'Look, I'll have to skip coffee. I'm due back in five minutes. See you Friday.' With a cheery wave she slipped out from the table and within seconds she was out of the restaurant, leaving a somewhat bemused Stacey to finish her meal.

It was a few minutes past two when Stacey entered the reception area of Paul's suite of offices, and almost immediately his secretary was summoned to escort her to his private waiting room. Such deferential treatment brought a faint smile to her lips as she remembered the manner in which she had entered these portals only a week ago.

She took a seat near the large plate-glass window and selected a magazine, leafing through it with seeming interest.

The sound of the door opening caught her attention, and she looked up to see Paul in the aperture, his tall well-proportioned frame exuding tautly-leashed

power, and she blinked quickly against the sheer mag-
netism he projected. Even just looking at him she
could almost feel the touch of his mouth on hers, the
memory all too vivid, and she shook her head slightly
to erase the vision.

'You've had lunch?' The query was concise, and she
nodded in acquiescence.

'Have you?'

His smile was entirely cynical. 'I had my secretary
send in coffee and sandwiches over an hour ago. Shall
we go?'

Stacey was conscious of his hand at her elbow as
they walked through the foyer, and in the elevator she
made no move to pull away. Once out on the street she
raised no objection when he suggested an exclusive
boutique several blocks distant.

With the air of a connoisseur Paul exercised undoubted charm to persuade the designer to reveal some
of her finest gowns, and Stacey was consulted only after
a choice of several had been made. Even then she had
the distinct feeling her opinions were heard merely as
a belated afterthought.

The final selection was narrowed down to two, one
of which she felt was ideal. Of silk in a dark shade of
burgundy, it had a softly-draped bodice, full sleeves,
an elegantly-styled skirt, and the colour complimented
her golden skin and lent her chestnut hair a burnished
glow. There was no price tag, and she sensed it was
ruinously expensive.

'We will take both,' Paul declared, ignoring Stacey's
audible gasp, and when they were out of the boutique
he led her the length of the block to another. 'Shoes,'
he said firmly.

From there they entered a nearby jeweller's, where

much to her horror a magnificent solitaire diamond ring was slid on to her finger.

'I don't want it,' she protested vehemently beneath her breath the instant the saleman was out of earshot.

'It is expected of you to possess one,' Paul drawled somewhat dryly. 'Consider it part of the window-dressing.'

'Rings on my fingers, bells on my toes,' Stacey accorded with a wry grimace. 'What next?'

'A gold necklace—a slim chain, I think. Françoise suggested it as a complement to the gown.'

'I'll return it to you in one year, eleven months and three weeks' time,' she determined, and he gave a sardonic nod by way of acknowledgment.

It was almost five-thirty when the sleek BMW slid to a halt in the driveway, and Alex hurried out from the front door to assist with the numerous packages.

'We leave in an hour,' Paul indicated as they entered the downstairs foyer. 'Sophie will unpack everything while you shower.' He rubbed a rueful hand over his chin. 'I must shave.'

Stacey was ready with several minutes to spare, despite having to re-apply her eye make-up twice in an effort to achieve the right effect. She felt like a million dollars, and her mirrored image revealed a slender form she hardly recognised as her own. Her hair swung loose about her shoulders, and she toyed with it idly, drawing it away from her nape and bunching it together on top of her head.

'Leave it loose,' Paul directed from the doorway, and she swung round to face him.

'I feel more sophisticated with it up,' she exclaimed doubtfully.

'Loose.' He came close and pulled her hands down.

'You look too severe with it drawn back from your face.'

'You like giving orders,' she accorded with a returning trace of fierceness.

'I prefer—advice.'

She would never win any battles with him, and tonight she didn't even want to try. 'How many guests will be there?'

'About twenty, I believe.'

'I don't suppose I could have a drink before we leave?'

'Dutch courage?' Paul queried with a twisted smile, and she grimaced.

'I feel as if I'm about to be fed to the lions.'

'My mother may appear a trifle severe——'

'My God!' Stacey swore with incredulity. 'That's the understatement of the year!'

'Shall we go?' he slanted mockingly.

During the drive to Franston Paul revealed that Nicos would be home at the weekend for the August school holidays, and the thought that she would have company throughout the day almost made Stacey giddy with pleasure. Having someone young to talk to would prove a welcome diversion. The house was spotlessly maintained by a very capable Sophie, and the meals prepared by that good woman were a gastronomical delight. There was a daily help, too, who unobtrusively cleaned and polished beneath Sophie's eagle eye, and as Alex tended the grounds, there was very little for Stacey to do. Even selecting the evening menu was best left to Sophie's discretion. Consequently Stacey filled her time listening to the stereo, or idly browsing through the many books lining the entire wall in the downstairs family room.

At the number of cars lining the drive outside the

Frankston residence Stacey drew an inaudible breath, aware that this was no ordinary dinner party.

With idle curiosity she wondered if Christina would be among the guests, instinctively certain that she would. Mrs Leandros would ensure it.

'Paul, my dear, how well you look! Stacey.' That was added very much as an afterthought, and Stacey offered Paul's mother a brilliant smile.

'It looks as if everyone has preceded us,' Paul observed with bland urbanity, and Mrs Leandros gave a tinkling laugh.

'But of course. The guests of honour must always arrive last. Come into the lounge and have a drink.'

Somehow a glass was put into Stacey's hand, and she sipped the light amber liquid slowly. To cope with the evening she needed a clear head, not one muddled with alcohol. Glancing surreptitiously around the room she saw that it was even worse than she had suspected. The entire affair was an elaborate façade designed specifically to bring attention to Paul Leandros' wife. God help her, she was *it*, and she didn't much like his mother's devious scheming mind.

Aware of Paul at her side Stacey murmured in a quiet aside, 'I feel as if I'm on display—and as out of place as a catfish in a goldfish bowl! Could it be that your mother is trying to point out something?' she queried cynically, and caught his slight smile.

'Had you been of Greek descent and from a socially élite family, your acceptance would have been assured.'

She arched him a deliberately provocative smile. 'Possessing all the qualities of a carefully brought up, well-protected *virginal* daughter, in other words.'

His slanting glance held sardonic amusement. 'But you were, my darling wife. Much to my surprise—and delight.'

She felt her stomach somersault in remembered alarm. 'You behaved like a savage barbarian,' she snapped tersely, and was incensed by his light mocking laughter.

'You were not exactly docile, or willing. What did you expect?'

Stacey declined to answer, and felt her facial muscles tighten as a gorgeous apparition in flowing red silk glided towards them.

'Paul!' Perfectly matched lacquered nails—talons, Stacey amended silently—reached out and rested against the fine worsted material of his jacket, and the smile offered was totally seductive.

'Christina,' he accorded with polite civility, his eyes deliberately enigmatic despite the warm smile curving his sensual mouth.

She was beautiful—a fine-textured skin, porcelain pale; wide lustrous eyes as dark as coals, perfect features and a slender sculpted figure that would have looked elegant attired in sackcloth.

'My wife, Stacey,' Paul introduced with bland warmth, and Stacey was dazzled by the brilliance of Christina's smile.

'We had quite given up hope you would ever marry. Congratulations, Stacey, on having captured one of the world's most elusive bachelors.'

'Really?' Stacey's surprise was deliberately feigned, and she ignored the warning pressure as Paul's fingers tightened imperceptibly around her wrist. 'It was no battle at all,' she informed Christina sweetly.

Paul lifted her hand to his lips, separating the fingers as he kissed each one in turn, his eyes blazing down with an emotion that could have been mistaken for passion, but which Stacey knew to be anger.

'How are the mighty fallen,' he gibed softly, and with

a fixed smile Christina murmured something inarticulate and moved away.

'You're a cruel swine,' Stacey determined, hating him. 'The woman is in love with you—or can't you see that?' she added fiercely.

'Christina is in love with my money,' Paul drawled heartlessly. 'Marriage was merely an expedient means of acquiring it.'

'You have no illusions, do you?'

His look was totally cynical. 'None whatsoever.'

Stacey lifted her glass and drained the contents in one long swallow, and ignoring his directive to remain she began weaving her way towards the door leading into the hallway. If her absence was noticed—and she decided it would be—then she would plead a necessity to visit the bathroom.

Fortunately she knew where it was, and she made her way upstairs, the need to escape paramount.

Elegantly appointed, the room was large enough— the size of the lounge in their flat, Stacey perceived wryly. A tasteful mixture of wall mirrors, synthetic marble and mosaic tiles in muted shades of green, it resembled the epitome of luxury, with heated towel rails, concealed lighting, and a generous array of crystal bottles containing various creams and bath essences— even perfume.

Stacey sank down on to a stool and leaned her elbows against the cool marble, regarding her features with clinical detachment. Her mirrored image gazed back unblinkingly, and after a few seconds she wriggled her nose and gave a rueful grimace. No one would suspect those cool hazel eyes masked dislike and utter antipathy for the man whose side she had left only minutes before.

She looked exactly the same, she decided broodingly. There were no visible signs of the tempestuous physical assaults she had been subjected to, the emotional tumult Paul had caused within her pristine, unawakened soul. She hated him to the point of violence, yet no matter how she tried to remain unaffected, he was able to wring an unwilling response that mortified long afterwards. How was it possible to attain such heights in sensual pleasure with someone she hated to the very depths of her being? It didn't make sense.

'What in hell's name are you doing here?'

Stacey's eyes flew upwards and encountered Paul's ruthless gaze in the mirror, and she held it steadfastly.

'The usual reason one visits the bathroom,' she responded calmly, adding, 'It's polite to knock.'

'Be warned against deliberately arousing my temper,' he said implacably. 'If my mother or any of her guests suspect a disagreement, it will be you to whom the blame is attributed.'

Rage kindled inside her, flaring into emotive speech. 'You, of course, are the ideal husband! My God, you're detestable!'

'You have little knowledge what manner of man I am.' His voice was hatefully sardonic, and it was all she could do to remain seated.

'You care little for the feelings of others, and nothing whatever for mine,' she lashed out witheringly, and was incensed when he laughed.

'No?' His mouth twisted into a cynical smile. 'I could assuage my physical needs in far less time than our mutual—lovemaking endures.'

A slow tide of warm colour tinged her cheeks. 'I loathe it when you touch me,' she vouchsafed, her voice shaky with rage.

He moved forward with indolently graceful movements until he stood directly behind her, meeting her stormy gaze in the mirror with mocking cynicism.

Slowly he lowered his head until his lips brushed against her nape, then he trailed a seductive path to the edge of her neck. His mouth opened as he teased the hollows gently, probing the sensitive pulse-beat before moving up to nuzzle an earlobe. Not content, he sought the edge of her gown, easing it off her shoulder until the soft swell of her breast was accessible.

Stacey closed her eyes as the blood coursed warmly through her veins, and she gave a despairing groan as his hands grasped her shoulders, pulling her to her feet and turning her into his arms.

As his mouth closed over hers she stiffened in token resistance, then gave an inaudible gasp as a steel-like arm bound her close against the hard length of him, making her aware of his needs with shattering clarity.

His lips hardened, bruising as he demanded her response, then gentling as she became pliant in his arms, teasing provocatively until she clung to him unashamedly.

Stacey was barely conscious of the passage of time, and she experienced regret when Paul lifted his head. Her eyes held a languorous sparkle, her skin aglow from the effects of his kisses, and her mouth parted involuntarily.

'I like the way you hate me,' Paul mocked softly, and her eyes focussed sharply, dispelling the mist within which she had been immersed.

'We'd better go downstairs,' she declared a trifle unsteadily. 'Our absense will have been noticed.'

He gave a negligent shrug. 'So? It will be deduced that I am unable to keep my hands off you.'

The look Stacey threw him held a tinge of bitterness. 'That's true enough. You're a lusty animal,' she accorded hardily, and was enraged at the sardonic humour she saw in his eyes.

His fingers caught hold of her chin, holding it fast. 'Be glad it is you I desire.'

Her tongue slid over her lips, moistening them in an unconsciously provocative gesture. 'Take a mistress, Paul,' she adjured defiantly. 'I couldn't care less!' Her lashes lowered. 'Why not Christina? I'm sure she'd jump at the chance!'

'Undoubtedly. However, why bother when I have a wife for that very purpose?'

'I must pay my dues in full, is that it?'

'You would be wise to accept the inevitable.'

'I'll never be able to do that,' she said quietly, moving away from him.

In the lounge Stacey helped herself to another drink, conscious of the circumspect, some frankly curious, glances their reappearance caused. The evening dragged interminably, and it was a relief when dinner was announced.

The large formal dining-room was a credit to Mrs Leandros and her staff, for the table was exquisitely set with white damask, gleaming silver and shimmering crystal. Seating arrangements were pre-ordained, and Stacey noted without surprise that Christina Goulandris had been placed opposite Paul.

'What does Nicos think of his new stepmother?'

At the slightly barbed query Stacey turned her head slightly and met the openly cynical smile of the man sitting on her left.

'That's something you should ask Nicos, don't you think?' she parried, aware that Paul's attention was taken with something Christina was discussing.

'You're too young to be his mother,' the other remarked, adding quietly, 'He may develop an impossible teenage crush—fifteen-year-old boys are particularly susceptible to beautiful women.'

'Nicos seems to be a very sensible boy,' she responded steadily, and her companion laughed.

'Paul's whirlwind courtship has evolved much interest. Tell me, precisely how long have you known him?'

'Long enough, it would seem.'

'Strange,' he drawled cynically. 'Paul never does anything on impulse. Quick-thinking, startlingly astute, the man is a financial genius, in fact—but impulsive? No.'

'I think everyone is capable of an impulsive action at some time in their life.'

His silent regard held faint mockery. 'On the other hand,' he revealed musingly, 'Paul rarely makes an error in judgment. Doubtless I, too, would rush you into matrimony before someone more astute could snap you up.'

Her eyes were clear and twinkled with a touch of guile. 'Perhaps it was I who snapped up Paul.'

'Oh no, my dear,' he derided gently. 'He is far too wary to be unwillingly ensnared.'

Stacey digested this information slowly, then successfully diverted the conversation on to a less personal level, conscious with alarming clarity of Paul's powerful presence close by. He exuded a natural charm, his geniality and smiling warmth in total antithesis of the leashed savagery she knew to lurk beneath the surface on occasion. Did he display such unmatched passion with Christina? The thought sickened her, and she pushed her plate to one side, unable to take another mouthful.

It was after ten when they rose from the table and made their way to the lounge. Stacey was aware of Paul's arm resting lightly around her waist, the gesture proportional and derived solely for the benefit of the guests.

'I'm not a child!' she declared in a furious undertone, longing to wrench herself away from his side, and the glance he slanted down at her held mocking amusement.

'You often behave like one,' he drawled, and she flared impotently:

'You'd compare me with Nicos?'

'In some ways he is more adult,' Paul accorded dispassionately, causing her to snap:

'Thank you very much!'

His head moved to one side in silent mocking acquiescence, and Stacey ignored him completely, moving towards an armchair and taking a seat without sparing him so much as a glance. He, darn him, merely perched his length on the arm, sitting far too close for comfort, and she could have screamed with frustration when she felt him thread his fingers through the length of her hair.

As much as she longed for the evening to be over and done with, there was no urgency to leave, for then she would be alone with the forceful devilish man who was her husband, and she had no desire to be subjected to his lovemaking. There was a danger in allowing her emotions rule her head, for it was a luxury she couldn't afford.

Deep in reflective thought, Stacey didn't register that she was being spoken to until Paul's voice close to her ear brought her back to the present, and she raised startled eyes to meet his, meeting the warm affection evident with faint surprise.

'Darling, what were you dreaming of?' he teased gently, lifting a hand and trailing his fingers idly down her cheek, and she endeavoured to smile, conscious that several of the guests were watching them.

'I'm sorry,' she apologised, swinging her attention to Christina—it *had* to be Christina, she thought wryly.

The other girl's smile was a mere facsimile and nowhere near reached her eyes. 'A group of friends are organising an evening together towards the end of the week. There's a new restaurant that's just opened in Toorak that everyone is raving about. I wondered if both you and Paul might like to join us.'

'I'll leave that to Paul,' Stacey responded evenly, and it took immeasurable effort to retain a polite mask as Paul's fingers slid beneath the swathe of her hair and began a subtle evocative massage at her nape. He was doing it deliberately, and she hated him for such a blatant display.

'As long as it is not Friday,' he told her, his eyes seemingly indolent. 'It's the start of Nicos' holidays, and I always ensure we spend the first evening together.'

'Thursday?' Christina queried, sweeping her lashes in a provocative gesture. 'I'll ring and confirm the arrangements, shall I?'

Paul inclined his head, then stood to his feet, letting his hand slide down to capture Stacey's wrist. 'Come, we will bid my mother goodnight. Christina,' he bade formally, and when Stacey remained seated his fingers curled to exert painful pressure, forcing her to accept his direction.

In the car she sat in stony silence, staring sightlessly ahead as the powerful car sped swiftly back towards the city. Paul elected to refrain from any verbal recriminations, and she could only conclude that he was saving them until they were home.

Dear God, she was tired. Emotionally weary and totally enervated. If only she could go to sleep, and when she woke the two years of her life committed to Paul Leandros were over. But what then? It was doubtful she could emerge from the experience unscathed. Paul was far too dynamic a personality for her not to be affected by him. And Nicos. She felt instinctively that Paul's son was capable of capturing an affectionate niche that she would find difficult to discard. From Nicos her thoughts trailed to curiosity about his mother—who she was, and what she was like to have won Paul's heart. A shaft of emotion tore her stomach, bringing pain—something she refused to accept as anything remotely resembling jealousy.

'Overall,' Paul's voice accorded with barely concealed mockery, 'you behaved very well.'

Stacey came back to the present with a jolt, recognising her surroundings and realising in that instant the car was stationary in front of the garage doors. A slight whirring sound caught her attention and she watched in fascination as the doors opened by a remote control switch inside the car.

'You were insufferable,' she said stiffly as the car slid forward, and as soon as it drew to a halt she unlatched the passenger door and emerged to begin walking towards the internal entry to the house.

'Because I accorded you the attention and respect that was expected of me?'

'It was ludicrous and totally unnecessary.'

'And if in future I choose to ignore you, will you not complain?' he drawled, attending to the task of making both the car and the garage secure.

'If only you would,' she shot wryly. 'Leave me alone!'

'Continue to behave like a shrew, and I may tire of you.'

At the dangerous edge in his voice she turned and

said sweetly, 'In that case, Paul, I shall endeavour to be as shrewish as possible. You may own a temporary lease on my body, but that doesn't entitle you to my mind.'

His oath was husky, denoting controlled savagery, and Stacey wondered why she was impelled to goad him. It was pointless, for she never won whatever battle she instigated.

'You seem hellbent on unleashing my temper,' he evinced hardily, and his grip on her arm made her wince. 'Have you not yet learned that such an exercise is sheer folly?'

She stood still, and he paused to look down at her, his height intimidating in the confines of the passageway.

'I won't accept our—relationship,' she stated quietly. 'I can't. You possess every trait I dislike in a man. I don't care that you're wealthy,' she continued stoically, meeting his narrowed gaze with steadfast clear eyes. 'The qualities I consider important can't be bought. I'll live with you for the required length of time— I'll even endeavour not to embarrass you in front of your family and friends. I bear your name, Paul, but I'll never be truly yours. You can never earn that right,' she finished steadily.

His silence stretched endlessly, and Stacey experienced a feeling of unreality, as if they were suspended in time. When at last he spoke, his voice was enigmatic, his expression impossible to discern.

'Go to bed, Stacey. I'll be up later.'

Without a word she turned and walked on ahead, entering the foyer and mounting the stairs to their room, and once there she undressed with care, putting her clothes away with seeming dedication before cleansing her face of make-up and brushing her hair.

She was on the edge of sleep when she heard the almost silent click of the bedroom door, and she lay tense, becoming increasingly alert to the sound of clothes being discarded.

As he slid into bed beside her she deliberately regulated her breathing, willing him to accept that she was asleep.

In the darkness he reached for her, ignoring her thrashing struggles, and with a husky growl he stilled her verbal protest effectively with his mouth, her strength puny beneath that of his own.

Would it always end this way? she groaned silently long after the heat of his body had subsided. Paul could command her response at will, and she loathed him for that. More, she hated herself and her traitorous body for giving in so easily to his erotic demands.

Lovemaking should be precisely that—not a mere expression of physical sex. She didn't want to enjoy such a hateful exercise—in fact, it would be remarkably easy if it were that simple. But Paul, with every ounce of sensual expertise at his command, urged each throbbing pulse into awareness, playing on her awakened emotions with the consummate skill of a master fiddler. Loving him would be agony, and she had no intention of sinking into that intolerable hell. It was far better to hate him.

CHAPTER FIVE

'STACEY, what are you doing tonight?' Trisha's voice demanded from the other end of the telephone, and Stacey gave a light laugh in disbelief.

'Nothing—absolutely nothing,' she revealed. 'Why?'

'What about Paul?'

It was on the tip of her tongue to discount her husband, but instead she offered slowly, 'I'm sure Paul can get along without me for a few hours. In any case, he has a business meeting to attend that will probably involve dinner with his colleagues.'

'Perfect! I've got tickets to a play—I won them in a raffle at work. We'll have dinner in town first, okay?'

'Why not?' Stacey's heart lightened at the prospect of an evening out in her sister's company. 'Where shall I meet you?'

'Outside Myers, around six—is that all right?'

'Fine. I'm looking forward to it.' She replaced the receiver, then made towards the kitchen to instruct Sophie not to prepare dinner.

If Sophie registered disapproval, Stacey chose to ignore it, and deciding to combine her excursion into the city with a shopping spree she left the house mid-afternoon.

With tomorrow evening in mind, she elected to purchase a new dress, and she visited several boutiques before she found what she wanted. In black silk, it was daringly cut over her bosom, showing far more cleavage than she had previously worn, with a halter neck and almost backless. A cobwebby fine stole in black completed the outfit, and she exited the exclusive portals determined not to blanch over the exorbitant price tag.

There was time for a quick coffee before depositing her purchases in the car prior to meeting Trisha, and as she approached Myers she caught sight of her sister sheltering beneath a verandah.

'Hi—am I late?' she greeted, and Trisha grinned.

'No, I'm early for a change.'

'Isn't the weather wretched?' Stacey groaned with a grimace as she struggled to unfurl her umbrella. 'Shall we go for dinner? I'm all for getting indoors where it's warm and dry.'

They chose a charming French restaurant not too far distant, and after a glass of wine and an appetiser Stacey felt the warmth of the central heating seep into her bones.

'How are you getting on with Paul?'

The question came out of the blue, and Stacey took several steadying seconds before she chose to reply.

'Why do you ask?' she parried lightly, her eyes narrowing as she met Trisha's frankly curious gaze.

'Well, he's rather formidable, isn't he? Intense and rather ruthless—even cruel. Damon regards him as a kind of diabolical archangel—combining the power of a Celestial with the qualities of Lucifer himself.'

'Is that why you led me to think you were dating him—because of his purported reputation?' Stacey queried dryly, and Trisha had the grace to look shamefaced.

'I *had* met him once or twice,' she excused herself. 'Anyway, you snared him without any effort.'

No effort at all, Stacey added wryly, loath to reveal exactly why her marriage had taken place. If Trisha chose to think it was a love match, then she wasn't willing to disillusion her.

'Is he ravishing in bed? Gossip has it he's utterly fantastic.'

Stacey met Trisha's wicked gleam and fought the blush she knew to be colouring her cheeks. 'That's a very personal question that I have no intention of answering.'

'Shame!' that young woman accorded quizzically. 'You're a stepmother,' she continued with interest. 'I wonder what Paul's first wife was like? Was she Greek, or Australian? What was her name?'

'I really have no idea,' Stacey said coolly, thankful the waiter was almost to their table with the main course. Trisha's questions were too direct, making her aware that she knew very little about the man she had married.

The play was entertaining, but too bizarre for Stacey's taste, and they emerged from the theatre to discover the heavens had opened in the form of a torrential downpour.

Fighting their way to the car proved no mean feat, and despite coats and umbrellas they arrived thoroughly wet and bedraggled.

'I'm sick of winter—it's so cold and windy, and *wet*,' Trisha grumbled as she dried her face and began easing her coat of the excess moisture.

'I'll drop you home,' Stacey determined, sparing a quick glance at her watch beneath the interior light. It was after eleven, and by the time she delivered Trisha to Essendon and then drove to Kew it would be close to midnight. For the first time she gave thought to Paul's possible reaction, and pulled a wry face as she set the car in motion. He would be furious, without doubt.

Well, he could be as angry as he liked—she really didn't care a jot.

Driving was hazardous, and Stacey eased the car through the city streets with extreme caution. Consequently it was later than she expected when she brought the car to a halt outside the flat.

'Do you want to come in and phone Paul?' asked Trisha.

'No. He may not even be home yet. I'll ring you tomorrow,' said Stacey. 'Perhaps you'd like to come for dinner early next week?'

'Sure, I'd love to. 'Bye. Drive carefully!'

Trisha slid out and shut the door, and Stacey waited long enough to see she was safely indoors before putting the car into gear and reversing down the driveway.

The rain didn't ease, and alone the journey seemed to take twice as long. Traffic was minimal, which perhaps was just as well, and Stacey breathed a sigh of relief as she turned down the street leading to Paul's home. A few more minutes and she would be safely there, and the prospect of a hot bath and bed seemed idyllic.

It happened so suddenly Stacey had difficulty believing it, and she stared in open-mouthed disbelief as the engine faltered and stopped. Quickly she checked the petrol gauge, then the ignition, before twisting the key.

Nothing seemed to work, and after five minutes of receiving no reaction whatsoever, she locked the doors and slid out, pausing long enough to lock the last remaining door before setting out on foot.

It wasn't far, less than half a mile, and after a few minutes she began to run. Not through fear, she tried to assure herself, merely from a desire to get indoors out of the inclement weather.

She gave a sigh of relief as she reached the driveway, and her breathing was fast and ragged as she mounted the few steps leading to the front door. Uncaring, she pushed her hand against the doorbell and kept it there, willing Sophie, Alex, or even Paul to answer.

'Oh—*come on*!' she muttered beneath her breath, then gave a startled cry as the door flew open to reveal Paul against the background of the lighted foyer.

His angry stream of epithets was colourful and blistered her ears as he hauled her inside, then the door crashed shut behind her.

'By the living heaven!' he swore emotively, his eyes dark chips of pure jet as he glared down at her. 'I trust you have a good explanation!'

Stacey inched her chin a fraction higher, conscious of the water running in rivulets down her face and neck. 'I have, and just as soon as I've got rid of these wet clothes I'll give it to you.'

His husky oath was vicious. 'Where the hell have you been? I didn't hear the car.'

'That's because I walked,' she enlightened him, seeing with some satisfaction that he was momentarily lost for words. She bent down and slipped off her boots, then eased her arms out from her sodden raincoat.

'For God's sake, leave them there!' he snapped furiously.

'They'll ruin the carpet.'

'To hell with the carpet! Get upstairs. I'll have Sophie run you a bath.'

'You can't call Sophie at this hour of the night,' she protested, moving round him towards the stairs. 'I'm quite capable of running my own bath.'

'You are aware of the time?'

Stacey halted in her tracks at the heavy sarcasm in his voice, and she spun round to face him, anger evident. 'Don't play the heavy husband, Paul,' she warned stormily. 'It just won't work!' She turned and ran up the stairs to their suite, passing through the bedroom without pause to the bathroom where she pushed in the plug and turned on the taps over the large marble bath.

Within seconds the room was clouded with steam, and she wasted little time in discarding her saturated clothes. Adding a liberal quantity of bath essence she stepped in and sank down into the rapidly rising water, and when it was nearly filled she reached forward and turned off the taps.

The heat slowly seeped through her chilled body, and she soaked, luxuriating in the delicious scented warmth before retrieving a bottle of shampoo with which to wash her hair.

Afterwards she lay back and closed her eyes, enjoying the relaxing effect of the water, until a slight sound sent her lashes wide open, and her consternation at seeing Paul enter the room was very real.

'What are you doing here?'

'I seem to recall having had this conversation before,' he drawled enigmatcially, moving towards the bath with easy long strides. Calmly he reached out and took hold of a large fluffy towel. 'Sit up, and I'll dry your hair.'

'Like hell you will!' she snapped indignantly, and his eyes kindled with bleak implacability.

'Accept my help in the manner in which it's given,' he advised grimly, and reaching forward he pulled the plug so that within scant seconds most of the water had drained away. 'If you are to avoid a chill, the sooner you are in bed, the better.'

'You always command, don't you?' Stacey berated furiously as she scrambled to her feet, and she snatched a nearby towel and wound it round her body. 'You never suggest, or ask—you merely issue orders and expect them to be obeyed without question!' Her eyes flashed golden-green fire. 'I won't be dominated by a domineering brute—as you are,' she threw waspishly, then gave a painful yelp as he began to towel her hair dry, uncaring of her tender scalp. 'For heaven's sake, do you have to be so rough?'

'Rough? My God, I could take your slender neck between my two hands and break it—do you know that?' he muttered with suppressed violence.

'Why?' Stacey demanded. 'What's so wrong in my meeting Trisha for dinner and going to the theatre? It's all right for you to dine out and return all hours of the night. Why not me?'

'You should have telephoned me at the office.'

She gave a derisive laugh. 'And you would have been agreeable to me going?'

'What would you have done if I had said no?'

'Gone just the same,' she retorted swiftly.

'Even with the knowledge that you must face my anger on your return?'

'Yes, damn you! I won't bow down and be sub-servient—I won't!'

With an angry gesture Paul flung the towel to the floor, and Stacey lifted her head, smoothing the length of her hair back from her face with shaky fingers.

'I'll get you some brandy,' Paul said heavily, moving towards the door, and she threw him a hateful glare.

'I don't want any—I hate the stuff.'

'You'll drink it, even if I have to hold the glass to

your mouth,' he declared with grim implacability, then he turned and left the room.

By the time he returned Stacey had completed her toilette and was sitting before the dressing-table mirror attempting to pull a brush through her tangled hair. In the mirror his image towered frighteningly above her own, and a feather of fear spiralled slowly down her spine.

'Your brandy,' he grated, holding out the glass.

'You're incredible,' Stacey ground out between clenched teeth. 'Words fail to adequately describe how I feel about you!'

His silent regard was unnerving. 'You married a Greek who upholds many of the traditional customs. Feministic behaviour in a wife is intolerable.'

'You were born in Australia,' she cried, sorely tried. 'What you expect of a woman might be acceptable in Greece, but here, it's asking too much! If you wanted an agreeable non-argumentative wife, you should have married someone other than me!'

'Fate has chosen to tie us together,' he derided with harsh cynicism. 'Have you not heard it said that to win a battle, you must first fight? Is that not what we are doing?'

'I doubt we could spend five minutes in each other's company without it leading to a full-scale war!' Stacey wrenched the brush through her hair, angry that his careless towelling had amassed an endless array of knots. 'Look what you've done,' she cried accusingly. 'It will take ages to get all these knots out!'

'Give me the brush,' Paul directed harshly. 'But first, you will drink this brandy. I insist,' he added with formidable implacability.

Stacey was tempted to take the glass and fling the contents in his face, but one look into those dark eyes was sufficient to warn that his retribution would be cruelly swift.

In silence she held out her hand, then sipped the fiery liquid, shuddering slightly as it burned the back of her throat. With a choking cough she placed the half-empty glass down on the dressing-table.

'All of it, Stacey.'

The curt summons put a defiant sparkle in her eyes. 'If I have any more, I'll be ill,' she insisted stubbornly.

'You'll drink it all,' Paul grated ominously, leaning forward and picking up the glass from where she had placed it he held it to her lips while holding fast her chin.

'You barbarian!' Stacey spluttered furiously. 'God, I *hate* you!'

'You are beginning to sound like a record stuck in a groove,' Paul drawled pitilessly, and in an instant she was on her feet, bitter angry tears on the verge of spilling down her cheeks.

'I wish I could hit you!' she muttered in a voice choked with impotent anger, and his soft answering laugh provided the impetus to do just that, for without conscious thought she lashed out in utter fury, goaded almost beyond reason as she rained her fists against his chest, the only sound being her groan of anguish as her wrists were caught and held in a merciless grip.

'Stop it this minute,' Paul demanded ruthlessly, his eyes intently alert as he raked her stormy features, and he gave her a shaking that had no pretence of gentleness. 'Stacey, for the love of heaven, haven't you yet learnt that to thwart me is a useless exercise?'

'I hate you!' she thrust emotively, refusing to be daunted.

'In the dark, it isn't hate that sends you clinging to me with such abandon,' he mocked cynically, lifting her chin so that she had no option but to meet his dark sardonic gaze. 'Is that not so?'

She tried to swallow, but had difficulty because of the lump that had suddenly risen in her throat. 'I admit nothing of the kind,' she said huskily.

'And I, of course, couldn't evince concern as to your whereabouts for any reason other than anger, hm?'

Stacey stared up at him unblinkingly. 'Try—protecting your investment.'

His eyes narrowed fractionally and became bleak. 'You have the body and emotions of a woman, yet you think like a child.'

'How else would you expect me to think when you continually treat me like one?' she cried, sorely tried.

'You are my wife.'

'But hardly loved and adored,' she threw wearily, and a slight smile twisted his lips.

'No? Such a thing would be impossible, wouldn't it?'

For a long time she just looked at him, unable to discern anything but faint mockery evident in his powerful features, then she gave a deep sigh and attempted to move out of his grasp.

'It's late,' she said at last as an unutterable weariness settled in her bones. 'I must dry my hair. Please let me go, Paul.'

'Give me the brush,' he directed quietly, and when she made no move to retrieve it he reached out and caught it up, then with a gentleness she found difficult to credit him with, he began to restore order to the tangled length of her hair.

'Now, dry it,' he instructed when the task was completed, and without a word Stacey collected her blow-drier and plugged it in to a nearby switch, conscious that he was watching as she stroked the machine through her hair.

When she finished he took it from her, then picked up a handful of her hair and let it run through his fingers.

'It resembles rich brown silk shot with liquid gold,' he murmured, lifting it to his lips. 'So fresh and clean —a man could be forgiven for wanting to bury his face in it.' Idly he moved it aside to expose the creamy nape, and Stacey gave an involuntary shiver as she felt his lips trail a flaming caress to the hollow beneath her earlope.

'Stop it,' she whispered unconvincingly as his hands moved down over her shoulders to rest at her waist, then slide up to cup her breasts.

'Make me,' he husked teasingly as he edged the neckline of her nightgown down over her shoulders, and in a desperate bid to halt his disruptively sensual exploration she twisted out of his grasp.

'Another payment, Paul?' she asked bitterly.

'Damn you—*yes*!' Anger blazed in his eyes, to be replaced within seconds by pitiless resolve. Calmly he reached out and caught hold of her nightgown where it rested over the generous swell of her breasts and with cold deliberation he tore it right down to the hem in one long wrench.

Shock swept the colour from her face and widened her eyes into huge luminous pools of incredulity. The ruthless glitter behoved ill, and there was brutal savagery in the mouth that covered hers.

It was a long time before he lifted his head, and Stacey found herself taking in air in deep shuddering gasps, her mouth numb and impossibly bruised. With hands that shook she covered her trembling lips, too emotionally drained to hurl any retaliatory recrimination.

'If you insist on reducing our relationship to the level of mercenary payment, then expect to be treated like an ill-respected lady of the night,' he said ruthlessly. With slow deliberation he removed his clothes, carelessly throwing them over a nearby chair, then he swept her into his arms and carried her to the bed.

His hands and mouth were cruel as he taunted, teased, and deliberately roused the flame of her desire until she was a mindless mass of pulsating nerve-ends shrieking for the ease of fulfilment. Like a virtuoso he played each sensitive pulse, drawing the maximum pleasure, then culminated a crashing explosive crescendo that left her shaking in the aftermath of emotion.

It seemed inconceivable that one man could wreak such havoc, and in that moment Stacey truly wished to die. In a daze she wondered where she would find the strength ever to be free, for such freedom would only bring loss—a loss she doubted she could live with. The fight, the anger—it deflected from herself as she struggled to prevent her wayward emotions becoming involved. But it was too late—far too late, and a single tear rolled slowly down her cheek at the revelation.

With an angry curse Paul pulled the blankets into place, then reached out and switched off the lamp. She longed for some measure of comfort, but could not have sought it at that moment had her life depended on it, and in the darkness the tears slowly slid on to her pillow until sheer exhaustion brought merciful oblivion in the form of sleep.

Stacey dressed with care, affording more than usual time over her make-up, and her reflected image revealed that the effort had been worth it. The vivid green silk of her dress highlighted her chestnut hair, and the cunningly-cut lines revealed her slender curves to their best advantage. Stiletto-heeled shoes showed her slim legs and gave her added height, and the gossamer-fine wool stole she draped round her shoulders lent an ethereal air.

'Ready?'

At the sound of that deep drawl she turned and gave an acquiescent nod, then collecting up an evening purse she stepped towards the elegantly-attired man standing several feet distant.

As she drew close Paul reached a hand inside his jacket pocket and withdrew a slim jeweller's case.

'I have something for you.' The slight snap was followed by a slithering sound as he threw the empty case down on to the counterpane, then his hands touched her neck, sweeping aside the heavy swathe of her hair as he fastened the clasp.

Stacey looked down and saw the single teardrop diamond nestling in the valley between the soft swell of her breasts, and raised solemn eyes to his. 'Thank you,' she said quietly. 'It's beautiful.'

His dark gaze sharpened as he regarded her thoughtfully, then he trailed an idle finger over the length of the slender gold chain that held the diamond. 'Such docility,' he mocked softly. 'Are you feeling unwell?'

She was silent for several seconds, then she said soberly, 'You teach a painful lesson, Paul.'

'There are times when you drive me to the very brink of reason,' he revealed dryly. 'Shall we go?'

Stacey preceded him from the room, and as she began to descend the curving staircase his hand reached out and caught hold of her elbow and held it until she was safely seated in the car.

'Are we meeting Christina at the restaurant?' she

asked as the powerful car slid into the main stream of traffic.

'Polite conversation—or curiosity?' Paul drawled.

'Does it matter?'

'The restaurant,' he told her, sparing her a quick glance. 'The fare is Greek, as is the music. You may find it will be an entertaining evening.'

Entertaining? With Christina one of their party? It would be all of that, she thought wryly. Perhaps the other woman had chosen the location deliberately in an attempt to convince Paul he had made a disastrous mistake in not choosing one of his own countrywomen for a wife. His second wife, she amended silently, unable to prevent her thoughts from pondering over details regarding his first marriage. She longed to ask, but couldn't bring herself to for fear it would reveal unnecessary interest.

Parking was achieved with the minimum of effort, and beyond the bland façade the interior provided a startling contrast that was visually pleasing and had the effect of transporting the clientele into the very essence of Greek locale.

On guitar and bouzouki, four men drew out lilting ethnic music, accompanied by a female singer. Waiters and waitresses were attired in national costume, and only a few tables remained unfilled.

'Christina and her friends are already here,' Paul indicated, and Stacey schooled her features into a polite smile as the waiter preceded them to a table on the far side of the room.

'Paul! We've been expecting you!' a light feminine voice greeted. 'Stacey, you look charming.'

Stacey reserved her judgment on that particular remark, choosing to accept it in the manner it appeared to be given, not doubting for a moment that Christina's swift encompassing appraisal had calculated and assessed the cost of every visible item she was wearing.

Introductions complete, they were seated, Paul accepting without a qualm the chair next to Christina, and Stacey sat to his right, accepting the glass of *ouzo* placed before her.

From the onset Christina deliberately sought to make Stacey feel ill at ease, although she chose a subtle method that went unnoticed by everyone else. The various Greek dishes were a mystery that required careful perusal of the menu before she felt content to make her selection, and when it came to dessert she allowed Paul to order for her.

The conversation frequently lapsed into Greek, led more often than not by Christina, and although Stacey tried not to let it rankle, nonetheless it did, and she subsided into silence, feeling more and more like a fish out of water as the evening progressed.

'Would you like to dance?'

Stacey looked carefully at her husband, then veiling her eyes she responded with cool politeness, 'I'm unfamiliar with Greek dancing.'

'It is possible that later there will be some traditional dancing,' Paul drawled, his eyes hooded as he regarded her. 'But that is conducted by the men.'

'Why not ask Christina? I'm sure she will be more appreciative of your favours.' Oh, what was the matter with her? She longed to be in his arms, so why refuse?

'I prefer to ask you.'

'Why?' she demanded baldly, and coloured beneath his darkly quizzical gaze.

'Do you really want me to tell you?' he drawled with teasing cynicism, letting his eyes rove intimately over her expressive features, so that she felt as if his lips actually touched her mouth and the vulnerable pulse that was already beating crazily at the base of her throat.

It was a blatant display of ownership, and she resented being made the scapegoat. She longed to refuse, but to do so would draw attention, and she was damned if she would give Christina the satisfaction of sensing discord.

'Very well,' she capitulated, conscious that Paul had already risen to his feet, and when she slipped into his arms seconds later there was a deep ache in the pit of her stomach. The temptation to rest her head against the broadness of his chest was difficult to ignore, and her hand moved restlessly as she strove to make her body stiff and unresponsive.

'You are not enjoying yourself?'

The query was quietly spoken close to her ear, and if it hadn't been for the slight taunting quality in his voice she would have swallowed her pride and given an assurance to the contrary. 'I'm not accustomed to being ignored by my escort,' she said stiffly.

'You want me to show you more attention, is that it?' His breath fanned her forehead, then he demanded softly, 'Look at me.'

Stacey kept her head bent, and was unprepared for the firm fingers that lifted her chin and held it fast. His eyes were incredibly dark, their expression enigmatic. Gently his mouth touched hers as he traced the outline of her lips with his tongue.

'Don't!' she found herself pleading, her eyes shadowed and strangely hurt.

'One minute you accuse me of neglecting you, yet the next I am being asked to desist,' he mocked. 'What a contrary child you are!'

'I'm not a child,' she said wretchedly. 'And stop

playing with me! I feel enough of a fool, without you adding to it.'

'Why should you feel the fool?' His eyes narrowed. 'Answer me.'

How could she accuse Christina with no evidence? There was even a possibility she was being super-sensitive about the whole thing, anyway. 'I have a Greek husband whom I've known a total of six days,' she relayed carefully. 'The restaurant is Greek, you speak the language I have no knowledge of, and every-one at our table is a fellow-countryman. Is it any won-der I feel out of place?' she finished reasonably.

Paul regarded her silently for several seconds, and she had the strangest feeling he could read into her mind. 'Is that a roundabout way of declaring you want to learn something of our customs? Or is it merely pique that Christina contrives to show you to be the antithesis of herself?'

'You noticed,' she said with resignation. How could she have thought he wouldn't? Little or nothing escaped him.

'Christina is a family friend of many years' standing,' Paul elaborated wryly. 'I'm not blind to the fact that she fancied herself in the role of my wife. It's to be ex-pected that she resents you.'

'If only she realised how welcome she is to you!' Stacey sallied, and he slanted a cynical smile.

'Poor Stacey,' he mocked lightly. 'Confined to a two-year sentence with a man you hate.'

'Yes,' she acknowledged emphatically. But was it hate? Her emotions were involved to a point where they swirled into a heady vortex—she had only to look at him for that strange curling sensation to begin.

When they returned to the table Christina was nowhere in sight, and Stacey breathed a sigh of relief that was short lived as the other girl reappeared in company with her partner to demand within minutes that Paul should dance the next number.

If it was meant to cause jealousy, it succeeded, much to Stacey's chagrin! The sight of Christina in Paul's arms was akin to experiencing a stab in the heart, and she cursed herself several times for being an utter fool. Why should she care if Paul danced with another woman—any woman, for that matter? He was a brute, a hateful merciless devil, for whom she could never feel any affection. As far as she was concerned, Christina could have him!

When one of the men in their group asked Stacey to dance she accepted without thought, only to have Paul intervene smoothly:

'You will not object, my friend, if I refuse permission?' His smile didn't quite reach his eyes. 'If my wife wishes to dance, it will be with me alone. You understand?'

The man's answering smile was tinged with a certain wryness. 'Of course, Paul.' His light laugh was expressive, and his eyes swept towards Stacey with sudden comprehension before returning to the cynically-set features of her husband. 'If she were my wife, I wouldn't let her out of my sight.'

Paul inclined his head in mocking acquiescence. 'I am relieved you are in agreement,' he accorded dryly, then reaching out he caught hold of Stacey's wrist and carried it to his lips, his eyes glittering dangerously as he dared her to defy him. 'Come, darling, let us dance.'

Stacey longed to hit him, and for a moment she contemplated doing just that, then returning sanity squashed the impulse. The look she shot him would have quelled a lesser man, even tempered with the smile she gave for the benefit of the interested on-lookers, but once on the floor she held herself rigidly away from him, her eyes glittery with barely suppressed fury.

'Did you have to be so—— Oh!' she hissed wrath-fully. 'You're incredible!'

'Is that all?' Paul mocked. 'Are you temporarily at a loss for words to hurl in abuse of me?'

'You danced with Christina!' she threw vehemently. 'Why shouldn't I dance with someone else?'

'You are my wife,' he stated indisputably.

'My God, I don't believe any of this!' she argued wildly. 'How typical of a man to impose the double standard!'

'If you object to me dancing with another woman, you only have to say so.'

'I don't care,' she tossed angrily. 'I never will. You leave me *cold*! Doesn't that bother you?'

His smile was humourless, and tinged with sardonic cynicism. 'Not when I retain such a vivid memory of how you react in my arms.'

Stacey felt the colour leave her face, and her eyes darkened until they resembled huge deep pools. 'You devil,' she whispered bitterly.

'Yet it is true,' he said softly. 'Why deny that in bed we are in accord, hm?' His eyes lightened with devilish laughter. 'For so untutored an innocent, you learn very quickly. The initial reticence—it is gone, is it not?'

A wave of sickness swept over her as the truth of his words sank in. 'I want to go home,' she declared shakily, determined in her resolve. 'I'll get a taxi.'

'We will leave together.'

'Now?'

His shrug was negligible. 'Why not?'

'But your friends—Christina——'

'They will assume I cannot wait to get you into bed,' Paul said wryly, and Stacey uttered a bitter laugh.

'They would be right. You're very physical, aren't you?'

'Are you complaining?'

'Yes—damn you! It would be something of a change to go to sleep without first having to suffer your advances!'

'Be glad of it,' he told her hatefully. 'To be a woman and undesired is an unenviable fate.'

'You really are the limit, do you know that?' Stacey choked. 'Oh, let's get out of here,' she cried wretchedly, almost at the end of her endurance. The entire evening had been fraught with impossible undercurrents, and she was scarcely aware of Paul's murmured excuses, the speculative glances when they returned to their table.

It was a relief to slip into the car, and she leaned well back in the seat, her eyes fixed on some indefinable point directly ahead as he deftly urged the luxurious vehicle through the stream of traffic.

CHAPTER SIX

'I'M going to bed,' Stacey murmured the instant she had preceded Paul through the front door.

'You don't wish to share a nightcap with me?' he queried sardonically as he moved towards the lounge, and she shook her head. 'Very well, little rabbit,' he directed, 'run upstairs. I'll be there shortly.'

'I shall probably be asleep,' she flung trenchantly, and heard his mocking laughter.

'In that case, it will be my pleasure to wake you.'

The look she cast him was full of venom. 'When will you learn that I loathe you to touch me?'

Paul's mouth twisted into a cynical smile. 'When will you cease being a child?' he parried smoothly, his eyes agleam with sardonic amusement, and without a word she turned and ran towards the stairs, and didn't pause until she reached their bedroom.

Undressing with unnecessary haste, Stacey donned the long silk nightgown that reposed beneath her pillow, then hurried through to the bathroom to remove her make-up and brush her teeth.

Five minutes later she lay between the sheets, the bedlamp switched off, willing her tense muscles to relax. With an angry toss she changed position, then plumped her pillow in an attempt to cull comfort.

Her ears were attuned to the slightest sound, unconsciously waiting for the almost silent click of the bedroom door. If Paul touched her, she would fight like a cornered vixen, she resolved with bitter enmity. He was so obviously in command, self-assured and possessive—so sure of *her*, she longed to hit out, to fight and scratch and generally vent her fury against him. Never in her life could she ever remember being so angry, nor so moved to anger by anyone. Paul Leandros struck sparks so volatile there was an instantaneous explosion whenever they were in each other's company for more than a few scant minutes.

Stacey's breath caught in her throat as she heard Paul enter the room, and she forced herself to breath evenly. Maybe if he thought she was asleep he would leave her alone.

Whatever hopes she had died an instant death seconds after the mattress depressed with his weight, and his throaty chuckle at her ineffectual struggles incensed her, so that she lashed out, fists flailing, and when that failed to register she took immense satisfaction from sinking sharp teeth into strong sinew and muscle.

'Hellcat!' Paul accused grimly, wrenching her face away from his shoulder.

'What did you expect?' Stacey breathed furiously. 'That I should lie back, accept your unwelcome attentions, and fuse my brain with thoughts of home and country? Ouch!' The scream tore from her throat as pain seared through one soft creamy breast. 'You barbarian—you bit me!'

'I merely returned your—salutation, in kind,' Paul husked, thwarting any attempts she made to retaliate by catching hold of her wrists and twisting them behind her back.

'At least let me fight!' she panted, struggling to get free, and discovering much to her chagrin that she was half sitting, half lying on top of him.

'My darling wife, I have no desire to fight you,' he drawled significantly.

'I know what you desire,' she threw bitterly as she wriggled fruitlessly to evade the trailing fingers that outlined the provocative curves of her heaving breasts. 'Oh!' she cried, enraged, as he began to tease each nipple until they burgeoned and swelled beneath his touch. 'You have the sexual appetite of an animal!'

'How would you define your response?' he taunted softly, placing a hand beneath the heavy swathe of hair at her nape and pulling her down towards him.

His mouth teased an evocative trail, exacting sensual pleasure mixed with pain where seconds before his fingers had been, and she gave a moan that was half-ecstasy, part anguish as he slid the straps down over her shoulders.

'Why the hell did you put this thing on?' he murmured thickly.

'I'd wear a straitjacket if I thought it would—oh, God!' she choked as the garment tore with a slithering whisper. 'Don't you have any regard for how much that cost?'

'No,' he drawled, unrepentant, and curving her body close to his hard muscular frame he rolled their combined weight so that she lay beneath him.

'You fiend,' she accused in a low voice choked with loathing. 'Oh, for heaven's sake, get it over and done with!'

For an instant he was still, every muscle tensed with anger, and Stacey caught her breath in fear of what form his retaliation might take.

'I am tempted to do just that,' he ground out. 'But even in anger, I refuse to treat you like a street woman hired for that specific purpose. Instead, it shall be you who cries for the merciful release my body can give, and believe me, I shall see that you *beg*,' he threatened ominously.

It was a long time before Stacey lay alone and ex-hausted, the humiliating sound of her cries echoing in her ears like the wailing of the damned. Her entire body had come tinglingly alive beneath Paul's deliber-ately erotic touch as his mouth and hands wreaked havoc with every sensitive nerve-end, every pulse beat, and she *ached*, body and soul, her emotions in shreds, tears of self-degradation and pity spilling and running to soak the pillow beneath her cheek. A master of sensual expertise, he had coaxed and honed her re-sponse until she moaned and begged, her pleas uttered with gutteral frenzy as she behaved like the animal she had so rashly accused him of being.

As she fell into an exhausted sleep her dreams were charged with pursuit and tortured capture by a shadowy figure that defied recognition, and she woke next morning to find an empty space in the bed beside her, unsure whether the protective embrace she had sought and received in the early hours of morning had been real or a figment of her tormented brain.

Nicos' arrival during the late afternoon was welcomed like a breath of fresh air, and Stacey managed to pre-sent a friendly spontaneity throughout dinner that brought an answering response from Paul, and to-gether, she was sure, they gave the impression of domestic bliss.

It wasn't until after Nicos retired to his room that Stacey's carefully contrived defence began to crumble, and she quickly sought escape from Paul's inscrutable company on the pretext of being tired.

In the room they shared she carefully bathed, then, dry, she applied touches of the alluring French perfume she had purchased during a brief sojourn to the city that afternoon. Next, she donned a daringly cut lacy

black bra and matching bikini pants, then she slid on
an exotic black garter, letting it rest mid-thigh, red
rose facing outwards. She sat down before the dressing-
table and began brushing her hair, stroking it again
and again until it shone like burnished fire. Make-up
came next, subtle except for the exotic red she applied
to her lips.

Rising to her feet, she moved to switch off the main
light, then crossed to the bedlamp, preferring its
muted illumination to the brilliance of the many-
faceted ceiling bracket.

The scheme she had devised in the cold light of day
took a great deal of daring to carry out, and after ten
minutes of waiting her resolve had ebbed to the verge
of non-existence. It would have taken a few scant
seconds to don a nightgown and slip between the silken
sheets, but she had left it too late, for even as she
turned to cross towards the bed the door opened and
Paul was in the room.

Stacey stood rooted to the spot, unsure of his reaction, then sheer bravado took over and she effected
a deliberately evocative pose.

'If you'll acquaint me with your preference, I shall
do my best to accommodate you.' She met his narrowed
gaze and proffered a beguiling smile. 'Am I not to
your fancy, sir?'

His eyes darkened fractionally, then slid the length
of her scantily clad figure and back again. 'For my
amusement, I presume?' he drawled, and she afforded
a slow pirouette.

'But of course. I figured that as I've been bought for
a specific purpose, I might as well dress the part.'

'You correlate the position of my wife with that of
a—tart?' His voice was dangerously quiet, and Stacey
shivered, her gaze faltering before his.

'Last night you treated me——'

'As you deserved to be treated,' Paul responded hardily. 'I am master in my own home—remember that.'

'What about me, Paul? Am I not entitled to have feelings?'

'You bear my name.'

'You have no idea how that cheers me,' Stacey retorted, finding it hard to remain defiant in light of her negligible attire.

'Stop playing childish games, Stacey,' he ordered tersely. 'You do not even begin to qualify.'

'Should I take that as a compliment or a condemnation?'

Ignoring her, Paul removed his jacket and tie, then began undoing the buttons on his cream silk shirt, pulling it free from the waistband of his trousers in one fluid movement.

At the sight of his broad chest, olive-skinned with its dark mat of hair, the physical evidence of muscular strength, she felt the traitorous embers of desire begin to heat her limbs, and she shivered involuntarily.

'Either put on a robe, or get into bed,' he instructed brusquely, and she said the first thing that entered her head.

'Why? Do I offend you?'

'I suggest you do as you are told,' Paul began silkily, 'before I am driven to slap your delightfully rounded rear.' He undid his belt buckle preparatory to removing his trousers. 'We have more than an hour's drive ahead of us tomorrow, and you may find it uncomfortable if you have suffered a spanking.'

'What's a few more bruises when I already have several?'

Paul's eyes roved indolently over her slender curves.

'Battle scars?' He moved towards her and when he was within touching distance he leant out a hand and trailed his fingers lightly from one bruise to another.

'Don't!' she protested, and attempted to move back a pace. 'Where are we going tomorrow?' Reaching out, she gathered up the robe that lay nearby and quickly thrust her arms into it, all too aware of the wicked gleam in the eyes above her own.

'Pity,' Paul drawled. 'Although since I have seen what lies beneath that silky wrapping, the addition of it is infinitely alluring.'

Desperately she tried to distract his attention. 'Is Nicos coming?'

'I have a weekend beach house on the Bellarine Peninsula,' he informed her with a sight shrug. 'It affords privacy and an escape from the pressures of business. Regardless of the weather, Nicos and I endeavour to slip away whenever we can. During term holidays, I ensure that I am free of social engagements at the weekend so that we can spend some time together.'

'Just the three of us?' Stacey queried, startled, and tried to hide her confusion. The prospect of having to present an amicable, loving front for Nicos' benefit for an entire weekend was daunting, especially in the confines of a beach house and in each other's constant company.

'Yes,' Paul agreed quietly. 'We leave straight after breakfast.'

She suddenly had difficulty in swallowing. 'Then I guess we'd better get some sleep.' Hardly daring to believe he would let her escape, she turned and walked towards the bed, expecting at any moment to be caught against him.

It was therefore something of a surprise when she

saw him cross to the other side of the bed and slip between the sheets, and rather self-consciously she removed the black underwear, then retrieved a nightgown from a nearby drawer and slipped it over her head.

With a deft click Paul snapped off the bedside lamp and she slid into bed and lay perfectly still, tensing for the moment he would reach out, but after several minutes his steady breathing indicated that he had fallen asleep, and she relaxed slowly, unable to believe she had been let off so lightly.

But had she? she pondered interminable minutes later. How contrary could she get, for heaven's sake? She didn't want him, yet here she lay staring at the ceiling in the darkness, aware of a vague ache in her lower limbs. It was madness! Determinedly she closed her eyes and tried to concentrate on summoning sleep, but it was all to no avail, and it seemed an age before she finally drifted into that somnolent state.

The drive down to Bellarine took just over an hour on the Prince's Highway, the sleek BMW eating up the distance with effortless ease beneath Paul's competent hands.

Stacey elected to travel in slacks and a warm bulky jumper, and on the seat behind her was a fur-lined suede jacket to sling round her shoulders the instant she stepped from the heated car. Paul had deviated from his array of formal business suits and looked ruggedly masculine in dark cords and a thick Arran sweater. He too had slung a fur-lined jacket on to the back seat, and Nicos was similarly attired.

Conversation was relaxed and amazingly easy to maintain, and not once did Stacey sense an awkward silence. It was obvious father and son shared a close rapport, and she found it touching that Nicos sought to draw her into their family circle.

The beach house was hardly the small chalet-like dwelling Stacey had imagined, and she viewed the solid sprawling structure with faint awe. A wide expanse of plate glass provided an excellent view out over Port Phillip Bay, and inside there were several rooms leading off a wide central hallway that ended in a large lounge running the entire width of the house. Furnished with an abundance of cushioned cane sofas and chairs, scatter rugs on vinyl-covered floors, it breathed an air of casual elegance the Kew mansion could never emulate.

'Brrh!' Nicos commented, rubbing his hands together. 'I'll organise the central heating, shall I?'

Stacey looked faintly scandalised. 'Central heating—in a beach house? You have to be kidding!'

'Blame it on my Mediterranean blood,' Paul shrugged with a slight smile. 'I'll brave the elements without so much as a qualm, but when I relax I prefer to be warm.'

Nicos laughed, shooting Stacey a wicked wink. 'Heaven help you when he's a crotchety old man!'

I won't be around then, she longed to reveal, unable to imagine Paul as anything other than the virile, powerful figure he was, and she managed a smile, instilling a hint of mischief to her voice. 'Arthritic, swaddled in rugs, and tetchy?'

'I will exact punishment for that at a more suitable time,' Paul intervened with mock severity, and Nicos broke into undisguised laughter.

'I could always go fishing,' he suggested, shooting a surprisingly adult glance from his father to Stacey, and she turned away on the pretext of exploring the rest of the house, feeling strangely embarrassed.

There were four bedrooms, two bathrooms, and a large family-sized kitchen stocked with utensils of every size and description. Eggs, butter, milk, plus an assortment of preserves resided in the refrigerator, and the freezer was more than adequately filled.

'Everything is to your satisfaction?'

Stacey didn't turn round, merely closed one cupboard, then went on to open another. 'Of course,' she replied evenly. 'Although you must realise I am unfamiliar with Greek cuisine. I presume you require me to cook our meals while we're here?'

'We can always drive to Queenscliff and eat at a restaurant,' Paul told her with faint mockery, crossing to stand beside her. 'Neither Nicos nor I are exactly helpless,' he added with an eloquent shrug. 'We usually take it in turns to cook while we're here.'

'Really?' Her disbelief was evident. 'My experience doesn't run to Cordon Bleu,' she admitted, 'but I can dish up a reasonable meal.'

'Nicos and I will take the boat out after lunch. Do you want to come?'

Stacey suppressed a shudder and shook her head. 'I get seasick. I'd much rather stay here, if you don't mind.'

'As you prefer,' he dismissed. 'We'll be back well before dark.'

'I'll have a meal ready.' A slight frown creased her brow. 'What do you usually do in the evening?'

'Play cards,' Paul shrugged indolently. 'Watch television.' His shrug was eloquent. 'Talk. There is no set pattern.'

'What sort of cards?' Stacey queried with caution, and caught his slanting smile.

'You play?' An eyebrow arched quizzically. 'Poker?'

'In an amateurish fashion,' she acknowledged wryly,

shooting him a sideways glance. 'Although I guess you wouldn't hear of a mere female joining in?'

His mocking cynicism was evident. 'Why not? Nicos will be amused.'

'And you, Paul? Will you be amused if I should perchance beat you?'

'You think to hide the ace up your sleeve, hm? This evening should prove an interesting—experience,' he concluded dryly, and she wrinkled her nose at him, determined not to be intimidated.

'If you intend staying in the kitchen,' she threatened with mock severity, 'I shall assign you some chores.'

'I can think of one,' he drawled, bending his head down to hers. 'And it is no chore at all,' he murmured as his mouth hovered fractionally above her own.

It was a light kiss, faintly searching and frankly seducing—gentle, when she never expected to be accorded gentleness from this pitiless, unpredictable Greek.

'Shall I go out and come in again?' Nicos demanded from the doorway, his voice openly amused, and Paul gave a deep throaty laugh.

'Stacey was deliberating what to have for lunch.'

His dark gleaming gaze quite plainly indicated that *food* was the last thing on his mind, and Stacey inwardly writhed, furious that he did nothing to disguise his lusty appetite.

A light tinge of delicate colour crept over her cheeks, but in truth she couldn't decide whether it was anger or embarrassment, and with supreme effort she summoned forth a bright smile. 'Soup—vegetable, I think,' she determined. 'Followed by an omelette stuffed with mushrooms, bacon and onions; bread; and I daresay I could manage a passable dessert,' she concluded. 'Tonight I'll serve you a stew. The meat will have had time to defrost by then so that I can prepare it.'

'The heating has been switched on,' Nicos informed her. 'We should be feeling its effects soon.'

Paul thrust both hands into his trouser pockets and moved towards the door. 'Meanwhile, I suggest we go and inspect the boating equipment.' He placed an affectionate hand on Nicos' shoulder, and Stacey heard their voices fade into an indistinguishable murmur as they walked down the hall.

Lunch was a convivial meal, seemingly relaxed, and conversation in the main centred around the various fishing spoils Paul and Nicos had gained over the past few years. They ate with evident enjoyment, heartily clearing their plates, and when they left shortly after one o'clock Stacey set about clearing the table and attended to the dishes.

It didn't bother her being alone in the house, and when she had prepared the meat and vegetables for the tasty *ragoût* and it was simmering gently on the stove she donned her jacket and went outdoors.

The sky was grey and ominous-looking, clouds were banked to the south, moving quickly eastward, and rain seemed imminent. Stacey turned up the collar on her jacket and thrust her hands into the pockets as she scanned the sea's surface. There were two boats that she could distinguish in the distance, but since she had no knowledge of the type of craft Paul owned it was impossible to determine whether either one of the boats was his.

The wind was bitterly cold, and after wandering several yards along the foreshore examining the sand for shells Stacey turned and retraced her steps, reaching the path leading up to the house just as the first heavy drops of rain began to fall.

The interior was cheeringly warm after the bleak outdoors, and after checking the stove Stacey set about making a dessert. There was sufficient soup left over from lunch, and after the vegetables were prepared she went into the lounge and switched on the television.

Rain lashed against the windows and thunder rolled in the distance, lending credence to the worsening weather, and by six when Paul and Nicos hadn't returned Stacey began to feel vaguely uneasy.

The table was set and the food ready at seven when the back door opened with a gust of bitterly cold wind, and the sound of male voices announced their arrival. Relief washed over her, but even as she turned to greet them it was too soon to mask the edge of anxiety that was evident in her eyes.

Their weatherproof clothing had been discarded, along with their wellington boots, but salt-spray mingled with the rain on their faces, and each bore an exhilerated expression as they laughingly held out their catch for her inspection.

'Tomorrow's breakfast and lunch,' Nicos announced with satisfaction. 'Already cleaned—I'll put them in the refrigerator.'

'I'll get a plate,' Stacey said quietly, turning away towards the cupboards, and when she reached out another hand was there before hers, removing the plate and placing it on the bench.

'You were worried,' Paul drawled, his expression watchful, and Stacey shook her head.

'Of course not,' she denied stiffly, and heard his throaty chuckle the instant before his mouth descended on hers.

His lips tasted salty, and she couldn't move as his arms wrapped her close against him. There was leashed passion in his embrace, and when he let her go his eyes were alive with an emotion she couldn't define.

'Liar,' he taunted softly, and she turned away, supremely conscious of Nicos' interested appraisal of them both.

'Dinner is ready,' she declared stoically. 'Shall I serve it now, or do you both want to shower and change first?'

'Ten minutes,' Paul decreed. 'Hm, that smells good,' he added appreciatively. 'Come, Nicos—we will take a bathroom each.'

Stacey began transferring the food from saucepans into serving dishes, then ladled the soup into each respective plate, took the heated garlic-buttered french bread from its tinfoil, and tidied the bench before transferring everything on to the table.

Both men did full justice to the meal, eating with evident hunger, and there was a bottle of dry red wine which Paul produced to accompany the meal.

'You can cook,' Nicos complimented warmly, and Stacey swept him a smiling glance.

'Thank you,' she acknowledged, then added teasingly, 'Did you thing I might be a helpless female who couldn't even boil water?'

His answering grin was deliberately wicked. 'I doubt my father married you for your culinary abilities.'

Paul gave a deep chuckle, and his eyes gleamed with humorous devilry. 'It didn't even come into consideration,' he drawled, and Stacey fixed him with an unwavering glance.

'Dessert, Paul?' she asked sweetly, and saw the answering laughter in his eyes.

'I can't wait.'

Nicos began to laugh, and to show that she wasn't hurt by their raillery she wrinkled her nose at him as she cut the apple pie into portions, then transferred them on to plates, adding a generous dollop of whipped cream.

'Coffee?' Stacey queried a short while later, but was forestalled in her effort to make it as Paul stood to his feet declaring that he would attend to it.

'Greeks like their coffee very strong,' he added a trifle mockingly, to which she retorted with seeming amusement,

'How nice to see that you are domesticated—to a small degree, at any rate.' Her eyes sparked with deliberate humour as she baited him. 'I imagined you were impossibly traditional with regard to women— like children, they should be seen but not heard, and speak only when spoken to.'

His swift glance was impossible to discern. 'I was born in this country, remember? I like to think I mix the cultures of both to a compatible blend. You would disagree?'

Nicos looked from his father to Stacey. 'If you intend arguing, I'll retire to the lounge and watch television.'

'We argue frequently,' she informed him lightly, and was disconcerted when Paul deliberately lowered his head and kissed the vulnerable hollow at the base of her neck.

'Ah, but the making up is sweet, is it not?' he queried with a mocking lift of his mouth, and she had to physically refrain from hitting him, so incensed had she become.

His sardonic humour mocked her over coffee, and she was glad of the excuse to escape to the kitchen on the pretext of attending to the dishes.

Nicos insisted on wielding a tea-towel, and Stacey felt some of the resentment ebbing as he kept her amused with anecdotes from the exclusive boarding school he attended. Her laughter was unfeigned, often helpless, and in the ten minutes it took to set the kitchen to rights she had almost forgotten Paul's presence altogether.

They returned to the dining-room to find Paul seated with a pack of cards on the table before him. He looked relaxed and at ease, a slim cheroot between his firm sensuous lips, and his eyes as they met hers held tiny leaping flares that were impossible to assess.

'Poker?' Nicos enquired as he took a seat opposite his father. 'What are the stakes—ten cents, twenty?'

'Twenty,' Paul revealed as he began dealing the cards, then he reached into his pocket and withdrew a handful of silver, placing several coins beside Stacey's hand.

'I have my own money,' she refused, and made to move to the bedroom where she had left her handbag, only to have a hand on her arm bring her to a halt.

'Sit down,' he commanded, but she chose to ignore the warning that hardened his eyes.

'If I'm going to play, I'd prefer to use my own,' she insisted quietly, meeting his gaze steadfastly.

'You are a very stubborn woman,' he drawled, releasing her arm, and she proferred a slight smile.

'I'm an individual, Paul, possessing certain standards and ideals,' she said evenly. 'I won't become blindly obedient to your every word, simply because you expect it.'

The expression in his eyes belied the carelessly indolent shrug, and she gave an angry sigh as she rummaged in her purse for coins. She knew she was a fool to defy him, for his retribution would come later when they were alone, but pride and sheer dogged resolve refused to allow her to comply.

Nicos, even as a teenager, was a skilful player, but

uncomparable with his father, and Stacey found her pile of coins steadily depleted.

An hour passed, and another, until after losing the last coin in her original stake, Stacey decided ruefully to withdraw.

'You want to borrow some of mine?'

She met the faintly quizzical expression in Paul's eyes and laughingly shook her head. 'That way leads to sure disaster,' she refused. 'I would only have to pay you back.'

He took time to gather in the cards, shuffle and re-shuffle them. 'I'm sure we can come to some arrangement,' he mocked, his dark eyes brilliant as they rested on her.

Again she shook her head. 'No. I hate to be in anyone's debt.'

Paul's gaze narrowed slightly, then he removed his cheroot and crushed it into a nearby ashtray. 'You have no objection if Nicos and I continue?'

'Not at all,' she responded evenly. 'I shall enjoy watching to see who wins.'

There was no doubt about the eventual outcome, and Stacey found Paul's deliberate pacing of the game untenable. It incensed her that he should consistently permit Nicos to lose—not that the amount was a large one, in all probability little more than two weeks' pocket money, but it was the principle of the thing, she assured herself.

'You are angry about something?'

Stacey swung round to face Paul as he shut the bedroom door behind them, and her eyes were alive with sparks of anger.

'You really enjoyed that, didn't you?' she flung bitterly, standing ground as he advanced towards her.

'Fleecing my son of his money?' he countered with a measure of cynical humour.

'Damn you—*yes*! You knew you would win,' she accused. 'Did you have to do it so overwhelmingly?'

His eyes narrowed fractionally. 'Yet Nicos still played,' he reminded her quietly. 'He finished the game, knowing that he would lose. Would you have had me play falsely, just so that he could win?'

'It wouldn't have hurt you to lose!'

His penetrating gaze was totally without mockery. 'And in doing so, I would lose not only the game, but Nicos' respect. If he is to win, he knows it will be by skill alone—and perhaps luck.'

'He's only a boy,' she flung angrily.

'He is almost a man.'

Stacey raised her eyes towards the ceiling expressively. 'And he could do no better than to imitate your image, I suppose?'

'If he is to succeed, he must accept that it is necessary to strive for life's achievements, not that it is tolerable to apply little effort. You are aware of the adage "it is sometimes necessary to be cruel to be kind"?'

'A lesson in character-building, I suppose?'

He regarded her steadily. 'I like to think so.'

Stacey turned away, sustaining impotent rage, and when his hands curled over her shoulders she wrenched out of his grasp. 'Leave me alone!' She swung round to face him, her eyes flaring with bitter enmity.

For a long time Paul simply looked at her, his expression inscrutable, then slowly he reached out and trailed an idle finger gently down the edge of her cheek.

'For a while this afternoon you were concerned for my welfare—and that of Nicos, were you not? It was there in your eyes,' he said quietly, outlining her lips, then he moved to tilt her chin. 'Did you imagine the worst, and in so doing, discover that it bothered you?'

'You flatter yourself,' she decried, endeavouring to instil some conviction into her voice. 'Why should I worry? If anything happened to you, I would be free,' she finished fiercely.

'Am I so—difficult?'

'You're impossible!'

'Why?' he taunted gently. 'Because I find you increasingly irresistible?'

The look she flung him was full of derision. 'You could at least have some respect for Nicos' presence!'

One eyebrow lifted sardonically. 'You would prefer I behave towards you as if you were a stranger?'

'You needn't kiss me,' she choked, 'or look at me as if you can't wait to get me alone.'

'Satiate my insatiable, animalistic desires, is that it?'

Stacey fixed her attention on the shirt button immediately in front of her eyes. Put like that, the words sounded terrible. 'You're a very shrewd man, Paul,' she offered wearily. 'It isn't in your character not to ensure you reap the full measure of your—investment.'

'I could not possibly make love to you for any other reason, hm?' he drawled enigmatically, and she slowly raised her eyes to meet his.

'Is that how you term *using* me?' she ventured quietly.

'If that were true, I would not delight in acquainting you with the sensual zones of your own body, teach you to enjoy as well as give pleasure, or restrain my satisfaction until you were ready to achieve your own.'

A blush rose gallingly over her cheeks, and she lowered her head, grateful for the long curtain of hair that fell forward to partly mask her features. It would have been so easy to have taken the single step into his arms, yet she was incapable of movement, and the silence between them drew out until it seemed to become a tangible entity.

Then slowly Paul pulled her unresistingly forward, his arms sliding round her back to hold her close, and his mouth descended on hers in a kiss of such incredible tenderness she had to cling to him for fear of falling.

Of their own volition her lips parted, and she met and matched his increased ardour with an abandon that was totally without conscious thought.

CHAPTER SEVEN

SUNDAY morning Paul drove round the peninsula and down to Torquay before heading north to Geelong, where they stopped for lunch. Instead of returning to Melbourne via the Prince's Highway, he elected to take the long way round through Anakie and Mount Wallace, connecting up with the Western Highway at Ballan.

It was late afternoon when the car crunched to a halt in the driveway outside his elegant Kew home, and after a hearty meal he disappeared into the study on the pretext of attending to some important paperwork.

Nicos glanced at Stacey and effected an eloquent shrug. 'The wheels of big business,' he dismissed expressively. 'Do you want to watch television? Or would you prefer to play cards?'

'Well,' she deliberated, shooting him a warm smile, 'I'm not in your league as far as cards are concerned. What do you suggest we watch?'

'Sunday night is generally pretty hopeless. We could listen to some tapes downstairs.'

'Great idea,' Stacey enthused laughingly, and Nicos' eyes brightened.

'Do you like Donna Summer?' he asked hopefully, and at her assent he broke into undisguised laughter. 'I suppose you know all the latest disco steps, too?'

'It depends what you mean by "latest",' she grinned, and he caught hold of her hand, pulling her up from the chair.

'Come on, let's go!'

Together they passed an exhausting hour practising dance steps, then collapsed on to the floor to listen to a few of Nicos' favourite tapes.

For the first time in ages Stacey felt completely relaxed, even happy, and she glanced across at the young man who for the next two weeks would make life bearable. Possibly he might consent to accompanying her to the cinema, and if it didn't rain she could suggest they drive to Mount Buller and the ski-fields. A whole vista of possibilities opened up before her, and although enthusiastic she decided to proceed cautiously. He could have made plans of his own, and doubtless Paul would ensure his son didn't lack for holiday entertainment. There was also Mrs Leandros, Stacey added with a mental grimace. Nicos' grandmother would insist she share some of his time.

'Are you permitted to have some of your friends here?' she queried tentatively, an unformed scheme rapidly assuming substance.

'Providing I obtain my father's permission,' Nicos answered, frankly curious. 'Why?'

'I don't suppose it's your birthday soon?'

'Next week,' he revealed slowly. 'Are you thinking I might give a party?'

'What do you usually do?' she parried cautiously, and he made a slight grimace.

'There's usually a formal dinner at my grandmother's house, with a gathering of relatives present.'

'A bit stuffy?' she ventured, and was rewarded with a knowing laugh.

'How did you guess! Grandmother is very family conscious, and Dad indulges her.'

'Then let's not make any waves,' she said quickly. 'However, I don't see why you couldn't have both—a

formal family evening on the actual day of your birthday, and perhaps a teenage party the following weekend. Friday, or Saturday evening—whichever is more
suitable.'

'Unsupervised?' he asked hopefully, and she shook
her head laughingly.

'Well, expect your father or me, or maybe Alex or
Sophie to make fairly regular appearances.'

'We'll make up a guest-list tomorrow.'

'Whoa!' Stacey grinned. 'First we check with your
father, then if it's okay, we'll work on the guest-list.'

'And now?'

'Now I'm going upstairs to bed,' Stacey told him.
'I'll see you at breakfast. Goodnight.'

It was at dinner the following evening that the
subject of a party was broached. Nicos had been transported by Alex to visit his grandmother—a habit of
years, he had explained, offering Stacey a regretful
smile when she had suggested they attend an afternoon
session at a city cinema, and a date was made for the
following day. Consequently she had gone into the
city alone and spent hours searching for a good recipe
book featuring Greek cooking.

'What type of party do you have in mind?' Paul demanded mildly of his son, one eyebrow lifted in quizzical appraisal.

'A few of my friends—perhaps twelve, maybe fourteen in all,' Nicos said quickly, shooting a quick glance
across the table at Stacey.

'Ah—I see,' said Paul with a slight smile. 'You wish
to invite a few girls, eh? Why not?' He gave an indolent shrug, his eyes lighting with faint humour. 'I'm
not so ancient that I have forgotten what it is to be
sixteen. When do you suggest would be a suitable
evening for this party?'

'We always go to Grandmother's house for dinner,' Nicos stated, and was rewarded by an inclination of his father's head. 'That will account for Thursday. How about Saturday?'

'Limit your guests to twenty, and inform Sophie of your intentions so that she can prepare what food you require.' Paul picked up his glass and drained the contents. 'It is fair, do you think, to place a curfew on this party of yours—shall we say, one-thirty?'

'Great!' Nicos enthused, his lean face wreathed with a sparkling smile.

'Tomorrow evening we are to be the guests of Christina Goulandris,' Paul announced. 'You, Nicos, will attend also.'

Stacey felt her heart plummet at this news, unsure of what the evening held in store—but certain Christina hadn't extended the invitation through anything as banal as plain hospitality!

As she dressed the following evening the qualms she had experienced throughout the day seemed to have magnified into alarming proportion, and her stomach hardly belonged to her at all.

Paul stood before the mirrored dresser and adjusted his tie, his eyes catching hers in reflection as she put the finishing touches to her make-up.

'Nervous?' His voice was faintly sardonic, and she deliberately concentrated her attention on the lip-gloss in her hand.

'Of Christina?' Stacey parried lightly. 'Should I be?'

His shrug was negligent. 'I am not blind.'

Stacey paused momentarily and shot him a quick glance. 'What do you mean by that remark?'

'You are determined to see Christina in the light of an enemy—can you deny it?'

'You betcha!' she echoed silently. Aloud, she said

carefully, 'I doubt she will ever be my friend. But then you could hardly expect *friendship* between your wife and one of your ex-lovers, surely?'

His lips twisted into a cynical smile. 'Is it possible you are jealous?'

'Good heavens, no,' she disclaimed swiftly. 'Christina is welcome to you. After the divorce, I'll give her my blessing—in fact, I'll even lay out the red carpet!' The thought of another woman—*any* woman, sharing his life, his *bed*, was enough to send her heart pounding with painful intensity, and to cover it she picked up her evening purse, then turned to face him with a brilliant smile. 'Are you ready?'

His gaze was openly sardonic, and she could cheerfully have hit him. Without a word she crossed the room to the door, then made her way along the hallway to the stairs, descending them with more speed than care, aware that Paul was close behind her.

Christina Goulandris resided in the prestigious suburb of Toorak, and her apartment occupied part of the fifth floor in one of the many apartment buildings situated in a wide tree-lined street.

Within minutes of arriving Stacey had been introduced to the other four guests—Demetri and Stephanie Andreas and their teenage daughter Helena, and a man who had been invited to partner Christina by the name of Theo Kaspanos.

Christina was attired in electric-blue satin that hugged her curves like a second skin, and to give the woman her due she was the perfect hostess.

Dinner was announced after drinks and a selection of hors d'oeuvres had been devoured amidst a spate of sophisticated small-talk, and Stacey found herself seated between Paul and Nicos, with Christina ensconced at Paul's right.

Dishes of every description adorned the table, none of which Stacey recognised, and she tentatively took small portions, loath to appear ill at ease with unfamiliar food.

'You find the *pilaf* to your taste?' Christina asked politely, and Stacey murmured a suitable rejoinder. 'Do you like seafood?' Christina pursued.

'Yes,' Stacey admitted cautiously, aware of Nicos' faint anxiety.

'Then you must try this.' Christina spooned a generous portion of small golden-brown fried rings on to Stacey's plate, then added a quantity of what appeared to be diced meat and noodles. '*Calamarakia tyganita* and *htapoki me macaronaki kofto.*'

She had to ask, of course. Which was exactly as Christina intended.

'Fried squid, and octopus,' the other girl explained with carefully-disguised triumph, waiting for Stacey's expected expression of distaste.

'Of course,' Stacey managed with a smile while mentally gritting her teeth.

'Both are an acquired taste,' Paul put in quietly, and she turned to meet his enigmatic gaze with deliberate guile.

'Darling,' she smiled sweetly, 'some Australians regard snake as a great delicacy. Remind me to serve some when you come to dinner, Christina,' she declared with infinite politeness, and caught the other woman's hard stare.

'Isn't that a favourite dish of the Aborigines?'

Stacey inclined her head. 'They have a liking for witchetty grubs too.'

Christina effected a shiver of distaste. 'How—revolting!'

'Not really,' Stacey responded in all seriousness. 'It's

simply a matter of what you're accustomed to.' With
the air of one conducting a pleasurable experiment
she speared a piece of fried squid with her fork and
bit into it. 'Hm,' she declared, 'this really isn't too bad.'
Next came the octopus, and she sampled it, making a
similar observation. Both dishes were as Paul implied,
and certainly not to her taste, but she was darned if
she would give Christina the satisfaction of reacting
with revulsion. With determined resolve she ate every
morsel on her plate, and prayed her stomach would
cope, not daring to contemplate the consequences if
it did not.

Dessert was much more palatable—a honey tart,
melopitta, together with *baklava* and *bougatsa*, followed immediately by strong Greek coffee.

In the lounge Stacey was conscious of Paul close by,
his tall frame epitomising leashed power beneath the
fine cloth of his impeccably-tailored suit. Every so
often he would catch her eye and smile—a strangely
warm and intimate gesture for her alone that she was
unsure quite what to make of, until sanity prevailed.
It was all for effect, and she responded in kind, restrain-
ing slight feelings of bitterness at the inglorious sham
of their relationship.

With Paul within earshot for the remainder of the
evening Christina was unable to treat Stacey to any
barbed innuendoes, but the promise of suspended
battle glimmered briefly in the other woman's eyes,
and Stacey knew it was only a matter of time before
opportunity presented Christina with the chance to
air her weapons.

Nicos appeared to enjoy himself, and took kindly to
being paired off with Helena—in fact, it seemed as if
the two of them were quite taken with each other.

It was a successful evening, and if it wasn't for

Christina's presence Stacey would have thoroughly enjoyed herself. As it was, she sat warily, supremely conscious of her hostess's every glance and deliberately dissecting her every word for subtle vilification.

In the warm luxury of Paul's BMW she sat back and leaned her head against the headrest.

'Tired?'

Stacey turned her head slightly and encountered Paul's lazy scrutiny. 'Not really,' she discounted slowly.

'Had you ever tasted octopus or squid before?' Nicos chuckled, his voice frankly humorous.

'No,' she denied, and he laughed.

'Did you like it?'

'It was perfectly horrible,' she responded, wrinkling her nose, and Paul's throaty chuckle brought resentment. 'I'm sure she selected those dishes on purpose,' she declared.

'In the hope that you would react adversely?' Paul drawled, sparing her a glance as he negotiated the traffic. 'Am I to suppose you plan a suitable revenge?'

Stacey cast him a level look. 'No, that's not my style.' A thought occurred, and she voiced it. 'I'd like to invite Trisha for dinner one evening this week. Would tomorrow be all right?'

Paul gave a negligent shrug. 'As you please.'

Trisha accepted with alacrity, arriving straight from work the following evening, and Stacey welcomed her with an enthusiasm that brought forth a murmur of protest.

'Hey, we only saw each other last week, remember?'

'It seems longer than that,' Stacey rejoined in an attempt to hide the aching loneliness that suddenly brought a lump to her throat. 'After all, you're the only family I've got.'

Trisha's green eyes sharpened. 'But you have Paul now, and Nicos.' She slid her coat from her shoulders, and a faint frown creased her forehead. 'What's the matter, Stacey? Have you had a row with Paul, or something?'

Row? What she engaged in with Paul could only be termed a full-scale war! 'No, of course not,' she answered lightly. 'I miss you, that's all.'

'Well, I'm here now.'

Stacey summoned a warm smile. 'Yes, and I'm glad. We must see more of each other.' She took Trisha's coat and gestured towards the lounge. 'Come and have a drink. Paul won't be home for another hour, and Nicos is being diplomatic in allowing us some time together before he makes an appearance.'

'He seems to be a nice boy,' Trisha observed languidly, and Stacey concurred as she crossed to the drinks cabinet.

'Sherry?'

Trisha made a slight moue. 'Something a bit stronger, if you don't mind. I've had a hell of a day. Whisky will be fine, and don't drown it with ginger ale.'

'Since when have you taken to drinking spirits?' Stacey queried with a faint frown, and Trisha laughed.

'Oh, come on,' she protested, 'I'm a big girl now. Don't mother-hen me, for heaven's sake!' She accepted the glass Stacey handed her, then sipped it with a murmur of appreciation. 'Ah, that's good!' She moved towards a sofa and sank down on to its cushioned comfort with a sigh. 'I'm glad you asked me to dinner,' she began carefully, watching her sister over the rim of her glass. 'There's something I have to tell you, and I guess now is as good a time as any.'

Stacey took a mouthful of sherry and mentally prepared herself for the worst. 'Don't keep me in suspense,' she managed lightly, and Trisha met her gaze fearlessly.

'I've got the chance of a job in Sydney. It's well paid and I've accepted.' She held up a hand as Stacey opened her mouth to voice her disapproval. 'I know everything you're going to say—I'm too young; it mightn't be what I expect; what happens if I don't like it? I want to travel, Stacey. Not just within Australia, but overseas, and I want to start now! This job in Sydney is good—really,' she assured her sister. 'I've already organised accommodation. Pam's aunt owns a block of flats in a swanky North Shore suburb, and she's going to let us have one for a nominal rent.'

'I see,' Stacey said faintly, trying to hide her dismay. 'When do you leave?'

'You don't mind?'

'Would it really matter if I did?'

Trisha cast her a look that was surprisingly adult. 'Oh, Stacey, I'm not like you. All right, I know you had responsibilities—me—and you weren't able to do what you wanted. But I can, and I'm going to Sydney.'

'Well, I guess I shall have to wish you good luck. How soon before you leave?'

'I finish work at the end of this week, and we fly out on Saturday.'

'That's only a few days away,' Stacey protested in astonishment. 'I imagined you meant a few months!'

Trisha shook her head, then drained the contents in her glass. 'There's something I wanted to ask you,' she said quickly. 'Paul has more than one car, which means you don't need yours any more. Can I have it?'

'I don't see why you should,' Stacey said evenly. 'I bought it out of my own savings—besides, you haven't got your licence yet.'

'I will have it soon,' Trisha asserted. 'Actually, I hoped you'd let me have it so that Jackie could drive it up next weekend when she comes. It would be handy for us to have a vehicle, and seeing you don't need it any more, I honestly thought you wouldn't object.'

Trying to give herself time to think about it, Stacey offered slowly, 'I'll discuss it with Paul and let you know.'

'What will you discuss with me?' a deep voice drawled, and she turned quickly

'Paul—you're early!'

His smile was warm as he crossed the room towards her. 'Yes.' He bent his head and kissed her on the mouth, a brief but evocative gesture that brought a slight flush to her cheeks, and his eyes gleamed at her confusion. He caught hold of her hand, entwining his fingers in hers, and he turned slightly to regard the other occupant in the room. 'Trisha,' he acknowledged blandly. 'How are you?'

'Fine, thank you.'

'Another drink? Stacey?' Releasing her hand, he moved to the drinks cabinet and replenished their glasses, then poured one for himself. 'Now,' he began tolerantly as he turned back towards Stacey, 'what is it you want to discuss with me?'

She met his dark gleaming gaze reluctantly, forcing a smile as she answered lightly, 'Trisha is moving to Sydney.'

'I see.' There was little she could discern from his expression. 'I presume you have arranged employment?'

'Of course.' Trisha looked from one to the other, then fixed her attention on Paul. 'I'm leaving at the weekend,' she informed him steadily. 'I've just been telling Stacey that it would be a tremendous help if I could have her car.'

'And is Stacey agreeable?'

'She wants to discuss it with you,' Trisha said defensively, and his smile tempered the steely tone of his voice.

'Your last encounter with a car was not exactly a happy one, isn't this so?'

'I've never driven a Ferrari,' Trisha excused herself. 'I had no idea it had so much power.'

Paul lifted his glass and slowly drank half the contents. 'And your driving licence—you have it?'

'I go for my test on Friday,' she answered a trifle sulkily, and Paul's voice was deliberately bland as he suggested:

'Then Stacey will defer her decision until then. Ah, Sophie,' he acknowledged with a warm smile as the older woman entered the lounge. 'Dinner is ready?'

The evening wasn't exactly a success, Stacey decided grimly. Although on reflection she couldn't fault Paul, or Nicos for that matter. A gracious host, he ensured there was no lull in the conversation, but Stacey found it increasingly difficult to match his geniality and it was a relief when Trish indicated that it was time for her to leave.

'Alex will drive you home,' Paul stated firmly, and within minutes the BMW pulled up outside the front entrance.

'I'll ring you tomorrow,' Stacey murmured quietly as she gave her sister a hug, and Trisha nodded, then bade them both goodnight before slipping into the rear seat of the car.

'You found the evening a strain, hm?' Paul queried mildly as they moved back towards the lounge.

'Trisha is a constant source of surprise,' she sighed, her forehead creasing into a worried frown.

'Your sister is an over-indulged, spoilt little girl,' he said dryly, and Stacey rounded on him indignantly.

'Spoilt? She can scarcely remember her parents——'

'But she had *you*—who, in your infinite wisdom, sought to make amends for all that she lacked,' Paul drawled. 'Consequently she made one demand after another.'

'I did my best to provide as near-normal a back-ground as was possible!'

'A misguided best,' he drawled wryly, and Stacey burst into angry speech.

'You, I suppose, could have done better!'

'Oh, yes,' he acknowledged with a twisted smile. 'I would have slapped her hard—several times.'

'Brute force isn't always the answer,' she cried, sorely tried, and his expression assumed sardonic amusement.

'Have you not heard of "spare the rod and spoil the child"?'

'Oh, stop being so damned sanctimonious!' She stared at him for several seconds, then turned on her heel. 'I'm going up to bed. Goodnight.'

'Trisha is a survivor,' Paul declared cynically. 'You have no need to worry over her welfare.'

'While I'm merely a fool,' she flung with asperity. 'Maybe I'll summon sufficient courage to do the one thing that's all-important to *me*.'

'Run away?' he arched sardonically. 'I wouldn't advise it.'

'Why? What would you do?'

'Come after you,' he answered softly.

'You're a fiend,' she said shakily, too weary to fight him as he reached out and caught her close.

'Whom you hate—not quite so much, eh?'

Oh God, he had only to touch her and she was lost. Even now, she was powerless to resist his mouth as it sought hers, and she wondered how she could hate him so intensely one minute, then melt into a thousand pieces the next.

Her murmur of protest went unheeded as Paul swung her into his arms, and at his husky exultant laugh she buried her head against his neck, content to lie quiescent as he carried her upstairs to their room.

With Nicos absent for the evening at a friend's home in nearby Toorak and Paul secluded in the study, Stacey decided to spend a few hours watching television. The film looked to be excellent, and it was almost ten when it reached its conclusion. Neither of the other channels were screening programmes which held any appeal, and with a sigh she stood to her feet and switched off the set. She didn't feel in the least tired, and she decided to have a shower and then go to bed with a new paperback edition she had purchased only that morning.

As she passed the study on her way towards the stairs the door flew open and Paul strode out.

'What the devil!' he exclaimed, steadying her.

'I was on my way to bed,' Stacey explained, and he frowned down at her.

'Nicos? He is home?'

'No, he's staying over,' she reminded him. 'He'll be back tomorrow afternoon.'

'Where is Sophie?' he demanded, and she looked askance as he raked a hand through his hair, ruffling it into disorder.

'I imagine she's gone to bed by now. It's after ten.'

'Dammit!' he exploded. 'There's no more aspirin in

the drawer where I usually keep them. Have you got any?'

'A headache?' Stacey hazarded, and at his curt nod of acquiescence she offered, 'I've got some tablets that will do just as well. Shall I get them?'

'Please.' Without another word he re-entered the study and shut the door behind him.

How typical, she thought musingly as she extracted the phial of tablets and returned downstairs.

'What the hell are they?' Paul demanded brusquely as she handed him two in one hand and placed a glass of water in the other.

'Nothing that will do any harm, I assure you,' Stacey said evenly, watching as he swallowed them down. 'Is it bad?' she asked. 'Do you get them very often?'

'What is this—Twenty Questions?'

'You're a bear with a sore head,' she grimaced. 'Do you want me to give you a massage?' At his sardonic gleam of amusement she amended quickly, 'Just your neck and head.'

'For a moment I thought I was in for an unexpected experience,' he mocked, reaching out to catch hold of her arm as she turned away. 'If you think massage will help then I am more than willing to submit to your ministrations.'

For a moment she almost refused, angry that he should delight in taunting her, but with a sigh she capitulated. 'Sit down, Paul,' she bade. 'I need to stand behind you.'

'Have you done this before?'

'A head massage?'

'Utilised your skills on another man,' he elaborated with scant patience.

'Why should it matter to you if I had?' Stacey countered evenly, setting her fingers against the thick corded muscles at the base of his neck. Steadily she worked at easing the tension there, moving gradually up over the scalp to his temples, then back again to encompass his shoulders.

'That feels good,' Paul murmured appreciatively. 'Already the pain is easing.'

'If you just sit quietly, it should soon disappear almost entirely,' she advised, standing back a little.

'Can I request a repeat performance?'

'It isn't necessary.'

'The hell whether it's necessary,' he cursed ruminatively. 'Dammit, Stacey, I'm not one of your patients!'

'If you were, I'd tell you to mind your manners and your language,' she scolded heatedly, and was further incensed when he laughed.

'Then perhaps it's as well that I'm not. I imagine you were rather strict with your small charges, eh? Dealing out discipline with one hand and dispensing sweets with the other, without doubt,' he ended musingly.

'Some of those children had fearful disabilities,' she said fiercely. 'Wasted muscles that will never again regain enough strength to support their limbs, no matter how much care or encouragement they receive. Yet they never questioned their fate, or cried. A movement of an arm or a leg that we take for granted and is achieved in seconds can take almost thirty minutes of concentrated effort for some of them. Do you know what it feels like to have to ask a child to do something —a simple exercise, that you know will cause great pain? And have him smile, and do it simply because you tell him it will help him get better?' She couldn't see for the tears that welled behind her eyes, and she brushed them away with an angry hand.

'Stop it,' Paul directed, and with a husky oath he

grasped hold of her hands and pulled her on to his lap, cradling her head against his throat as his lips caressed her hair.

Stacey felt disinclined to move, and she sat there in silence, her eyes closed as she savoured the comfort Paul's arms offered.

'You miss the hospital so much?'

She considered the query carefully. 'I enjoyed my work,' she said slowly. 'Not all of the children were hopeless cases. Most were routine—simple exercises after undergoing surgery, or to restore muscle tone after the removal of a plaster cast.'

'But you were not able to achieve a state of total professionalism whereby you could alienate your emotions,' he stated gently.

'No.' She sat up and disentangled herself from his grasp. 'I'll go upstairs to bed. Are you coming?'

'Is that an invitation?'

A slight blush tinged her cheeks as she straightened her skirt, and she couldn't meet his eyes. 'I meant——'

'I know what you meant,' Paul declared wryly. 'Go on up to bed, Stacey. I'll follow soon.'

CHAPTER EIGHT

REFUSING to let Trisha have her car was one of the most difficult decisions Stacey had had to make, and she almost relented when Paul drove her to Tullamarine airport to see Trisha on the flight to Sydney. Although her decision rested more easily owing to the fact the Trisha had failed to get her licence the previous day.

Their farewells were slightly strained, and keeping the tears in check took every scrap of resolve, so that when she turned back to the car with Paul and Nicos Stacey felt an emotional and physical wreck.

She was scarcely aware of anything outside the window as Paul headed the car through the city and on to the motorway. They were to spend what remained of the weekend at Bellarine, and she had to profess to have no enthusiasm at the prospect.

Even dining out that evening did little to lift her flagging spirits, and she had to force herself to do justice to the excellent meal placed before her.

Nicos was an understanding companion, but by the time they returned to Melbourne the following evening Stacey could sense that Paul's patience was wearing thin, and it was a relief when Monday dawned and he left for the office.

A telephone call from Trisha the next evening allayed most of Stacey's anxiety, and after hearing how wonderful everything was, from the flat to Trisha's new job, she had to contend that Paul was right all along—her sister was indeed a survivor! Restored also was their mutual bond of affection from its temporary lapse, and Stacey was able to heave a heartfelt sigh of relief.

The next day Nicos suggested they take in a cinema matinee, and Stacey laughingly agreed, although his choice of film, an acclaimed war epic, turned out to be undeniably grim.

On reaching home Nicos invited her to listen to a new tape he had bought the previous day, and while the music rang from the speakers in muted electronic perfection he retrieved an album from a nearby cupboard.

'Photos?' Stacey hazarded with a grin as he turned open the cover. 'I bet you were a cute little boy!'

He shot her a wry grimace. 'Cute? Girls are cute!'

'Sorry,' she accorded with a self-effacing smile, turning her attention to the pages of brightly-coloured snaps. Then her smile faltered as she glimpsed Paul— a much younger Paul, with his arm encircling an attractive girl's waist, his head lowered down to hers and an expression of laughing devotion evident in his rugged features.

'That's Eleni—my mother,' Nicos revealed quietly, and Stacey nodded in silent acknowledgment.

'She's beautiful,' she said at last, aware of the sharp pain in her chest at the sight of Paul affording such tenderness. It hurt so much she could hardly bear to keep looking, yet she couldn't tear her eyes away.

'Yes,' Nicos agreed softly. 'She died a few weeks after I was born.' He anticipated her unspoken query and effected a slight shrug. 'Tragic, I guess.'

'Who looked after you?'

'My grandmother, until I was old enough for boarding school.'

'You're very fond of her, aren't you?'

'She's great,' he enthused, smiling as he caught her

slight grimace. 'Wait until you get to know her better. She always presents a formidable reserve with out-siders, but underneath she can be great fun—really!'

Stacey had mental reservations about her mother-in-law ever being considered 'fun', but she offered a non-committal smile. 'We're going down to Frankston for dinner tomorrow,' she said, assuming interest as Nicos continued to flip over the pages of the photograph album. 'Will anyone else be there?'

'It's hard to say. Sometimes she invites my cousins—the children of my father's sister,' he amended. 'But as they're coming to the party on Saturday night, she may not.'

Stacey's brow creased slightly. 'I don't remember meeting your aunt.'

'No—Aunt Lydia died several years ago,' Nicos ex-plained.

Somehow the thought of an intimate family dinner was something she would prefer to avoid, and Stacey viewed the evening with a certain amount of reluctance. Mrs Leandros was equally, if not more formidable than her son—a matriach whom it was impossible to ignore. The knowledge that she was not enamoured of her son's marriage didn't do much towards helping Stacey's de-flated confidence, and the prospect of presenting an amicable, even affectionate front was daunting to say the least.

As the sleek BMW sped swiftly towards Frankston she mentally reviewed the dress she had taken hours to choose earlier that day, fervently hoping the sophis-ticated image the mirror had presented only fifteen minutes before was not a figment of her fevered imagi-nation. Her make-up was subtle, yet alluring, making the most of her smooth skin and large lustrous hazel eyes. Her teeth worried her upper lip as she considered her use of eyeshadow and mascara. Was it a shade overdone?

Beneath Paul's competent hands the car covered the miles in seemingly no time at all, and her heart gave an uneasy thud as the BMW slid to a whispered halt ouside the front entrance of the Leandros' residence.

After an initial greeting they moved through the foyer and into the lounge, and Stacey was thankful that the occasion of Nicos' birthday centred most of the attention on him.

Sipping vintage sherry from an exquisitely-cut crystal goblet had a faintly soothing effect on her nerves, although Paul's presence less than an elbow's distance away didn't help matters much.

His attention towards her was that of a devoted husband, his behaviour impeccable. No one, not even the alert perceptiveness of his own mother, could have doubted that he was anything other than delighted with his young wife.

To give Mrs Leandros credit, she was a charming hostess, and apart from an occasional penetrating glance throughout the evening she accorded her daughter-in-law a degree of warmth, even the beginnings of affection.

The food was elegantly presented, and while indisputably Greek it veered away from the more exotic dishes, and Stacey was grateful that Mrs Leandros had thought to cater to her untutored palate.

Since it was an intimate setting for four, Stacey perforce had to converse, and she did so with polite reserve, speaking only when she was spoken to, very much aware of being an outsider.

'You are settling in satisfactorily, child?'

Stacey glanced across the table and met Mrs Leandros' look of faint enquiry. 'Yes, thank you,' she answered courteously. 'Paul has a very charming home.'

'And a great deal of money with which to indulge you.' Mrs Leandros' tone was bland, but Stacey sensed the slight barb behind the words and she held her gaze.

'I have no idea of the extent of Paul's wealth,' she said evenly. 'I don't place importance upon material possessions.'

'Yet it pleases you to receive them, does it not?'

Oh, lord, this was what was called the third degree! 'The receipt of a gift for a specific occasion naturally affords me pleasure,' she allowed quietly, conscious that both Paul and Nicos were regarding the exchange with musing interest.

'You will, of course, have children.' It was a statement and one which Stacey had no intention of verifying.

'Stacey and I have been married only a matter of weeks,' Paul intervened mildly. 'Can you blame me if I want her to myself for a while?'

'You waited long enough to re-marry,' his mother remonstrated. 'I had begun to resign myself to the fact that you never would.'

'Ah,' he teased, his dark eyes gleaming with humour, 'it is good to know I have pleased you.'

His mother gave a refined sniff. 'You always please me. Your only fault has been a pursuit of women in the years succeeding Eleni's death.'

'While I never purported to be a monk, my existence has scarcely been that of a hedonistic rake,' he chided with a measure of reproof.

'Grandmama!' Nicos protested, shooting Stacey an anxious glance. 'You are embarrassing Stacey.'

'Not at all,' Stacey responded with a calm she was far from feeling. 'I'm not unaware of Paul's past exploits.' She glanced sideways and cast him a warm smile. 'One couldn't doubt his experience—he is, after all, several years older than me.' She glimpsed the barely-discernible flicker in those dark eyes, and placed a gentle hand on the sleeve of his immaculate jacket, her expression soft and beguiling. 'Not that it matters in the slightest.'

'I'm thirty-seven,' he reminded her, the smile creasing his lips but not quite reaching his eyes. 'Thirteen years your senior.'

'My own dear Alexis was almost eighteen years older than I,' Mrs Leandros said with a slight frown. 'I confess I found his maturity beneficial—a steadying influence, in fact.'

'Actually,' Nicos began with the earnestness of youth. 'Stacey is closer to my age than she is to Dad's.'

Ouch! Stacey mentally grimaced, sure that the present turn in conversation was not well received, and she attempted to lighten it while still adding a certain sting of her own. 'Not quite young enough to be your daughter, Paul—unless you were ultra-precocious as a youth,' she added teasingly, and saw the promise of retribution in his answering smile.

'Are you suggesting I'm too old for you, darling?'

He was a thousand light years ahead of her, she thought wryly—worldly-wise and deplorably cynical. Something that had nothing whatever to do with chronological age. Aloud she answered, 'No, Paul. If I had anything to say, it would be to suggest I might be too unsophisticated for you.'

Eyes that were dark and unfathomable met hers, holding her gaze so that she couldn't look away. 'It was your very lack of sophistication that attracted me in the first place,' he answered dryly, and her eyes widened fractionally as she recalled that fateful meeting less than three weeks ago wherein she had not only hurled false accusations but insulted him as well.

There was a silence that lasted several seconds, then Mrs Leandros declared briskly, 'Let's adjourn to the lounge for coffee, shall we?'

After coffee Mrs Leandros indicated that Paul should pour them all a measure of brandy, and with a sense of ceremony a cake was brought in by an elderly house-keeper for Nicos to cut. Combining ground almonds and honey in its ingredients, it was topped with wal-nuts and syrup, and Stacey deduced from Nicos' pleased expression that it was a firm favourite of his.

Next came the birthday presents, and she extracted from her evening purse the slim eelskin wallet she had purchased that morning, handing the brightly wrapped parcel to Nicos with a sparkling smile.

They left shortly after eleven, completing the drive back into the city in record time, and Nicos bade them goodnight in the foyer before climbing the stairs to his room.

His absence made Stacey feel acutely vulnerable, and she glanced towards Paul, a murmured intention to follow his son on the tip of her tongue.

'Come into the study.' The command was brusquely delivered, and her brow furrowed slightly in perplexity.

'I'm rather tired,' she offered quietly. 'Can't it wait until tomorrow?'

His eyes darkened, then became hooded as he gave a slight shrug. 'The bedroom will do just as well.'

A shiver of apprehension feathered its way down her spine as she watched him extract a packet of cheroots from his jacket pocket and light one, watching the curl of smoke with fascination as it floated upward and dispersed. Without a word she turned and made her way towards the stairs, aware of his firm tread immediately behind.

In their room she turned to face him as he switched on the light, and the closing of the door brought a rush of colour to her cheeks that was galling. A sigh of resignation escaped her lips. 'Whatever it is you have to say, at least get it over and done with,' she said wearily.

'You imagine I am going to pounce, is that it?' he drawled, and she shrugged her shoulders in a gesture of defeat.

'Whatever you choose to do, I haven't sufficient strength to oppose you.'

'Yet you would like to do so,' Paul suggested dryly. 'You enjoy our verbal clashes, even when they end in physical violence.'

'There are times when I wish I could hit you,' she said bitterly, and he gave a humourless laugh.

'Am I so hateful?'

'Yes—no. Oh, I don't know anymore,' she ended wretchedly, and turning away she walked across to the bed and slipped off her shoes. 'We argue and fight at every opportunity.'

He walked slowly towards her, his movements lithely indolent. 'And make love?'

'That too,' she answered tersely.

'It affords you pleasure, does it not?'

Stacey spared him a brief glance. 'You make sure of it, don't you?' she answered wryly.

He reached out and drew her unresisting body towards him, encircling her waist with his hands. 'Would you prefer it if I were an inconsiderate lover who thought more of his own gratification than that of the woman in his arms?' he taunted quietly, and she made a murmur of protest as his head lowered towards hers. 'Talking is not what I have in mind.' His hands slid possessively down over her hips, hugging her close so that she was in no doubt of his muscular hardness, and she felt the familiar weakness invade her as his mouth fastened over hers.

There was a wealth of seduction in his touch, and soon she was edging even closer, the restriction of their clothes becoming an irritating barrier, and without conscious thought her fingers moved to unfasten the buttons on his shirt. The rough mat of curling hair felt springy as she slid her fingers over it, and her breasts swelled within the constricting bra, the nipples hardening until she could bear their restriction no longer, and with a muttered exclamation she stepped back a pace and quickly slipped out of her clothes.

Paul made no move to do likewise, and her eyes widened in silent query.

'You do it,' he bade softly, watching her expression with faint mockery. 'I have undressed you on numerous occasions. Now it is your turn to reciprocate.'

The thought that he might be playing some game of revenge brought a fleeting shadow of pain to her expressive features, and she looked at him in silent indecision, the seconds ticking interminably by until with a shaky gasp she turned and ran towards the connecting door leading to the bathroom.

She didn't get very far, and she gazed at him helplessly as he swung her round to face him.

'You idiot!' Paul muttered with dangerous softness, then he uttered a string of harsh expletives as he glimpsed the tears of humiliation welling behind her eyes. 'You think I meant to belittle you? Is that it?'

'How about—revenge for deliberately baiting you

over the dinner table tonight?' she managed shakily, and saw him frown.

'Ah, you sought to suggest I was some Methuselah. Old enough to be your father—almost.' His eyes glinted with sardonic humour as he took possession of her lips, and it was a long time before he lifted his head. Then it was to swing her into his arms and carry her unresisting to bed, and after his prolonged lovemaking she curled against him, languorous and content, like a well-fed, satisfied kitten.

The music hit Stacey with a cacophonous blast as she opened the door, and she endeavoured to hold the bright smile she had summoned only seconds before. Conscious of a few glances, she slowly and unobtrusively made her way round the room, replenishing crisps and nuts, checking that there was sufficient dip. Sophie was in the kitchen organising supper for the twenty teenagers, and Paul had closeted himself in his study for an indeterminate length of time after receiving a transatlantic call half an hour previously.

The party gave every appearance of being a roaring success, and as Stacey drew level with the bar she flashed Alex a conspiratorial smile. Elected to act as barman, he was the only adult present in the room, with the exception of herself. Strobe lighting, the very latest in LP's—in fact, everything Nicos had requested had been provided.

'Stacey! Hey, Stacey!'

She turned slightly and met Nicos' gleaming smile, her eyes softening fractionally as she glimpsed his obvious pleasure. 'Hi,' she greeted him. 'Everything okay?'

'Terrific! It's just great,' he enthused. 'Come and dance with me,' he pleaded, and she broke into light laughter at the earnest expression on his face.

'Me?' she queried with mock seriousness.

'Yes. This party was your idea, and I'd like you to have some fun, too.'

'Okay,' she found herself agreeing, and placing the large bag of crisps she had been carrying on to the bar she turned and followed his tall lean frame into the centre of the room. 'Just one dance,' she said laughingly, swinging easily into the movement required by the heavy beat music. Talking was virtually impossible and she didn't even attempt it.

When the track finished she made to move away, but Nicos caught her arm.

'Just one more. You really can dance,' he complimented, and she tilted her head to one side in silent acknowledgment.

'So can you,' she returned, following his lead into an intricate version of the hustle as the next track on the LP began.

Without any intention of remaining for more than ten minutes Stacey found it difficult to refuse when one of his friends asked her to partner him, and before she knew it she had danced with several, laughing, enjoying herself as she hadn't done for some considerable time.

'Oh, please,' she said at last, shaking her head when Nicos touched her shoulder. 'I think I deserve a drink after expending all that energy.'

'I've already anticipated the need,' a deep voice drawled from directly behind her, and Stacey turned to encounter Paul's faintly mocking gaze.

How long had he been in the room? With a faint smile she accepted the tall frosted glass of iced fruit juice. It had a very palatable smoothness as it slid down her throat, and she detected the faint taste of spirits. 'Thanks,' she murmured, meeting his dark eyes momentarily, unable to discern much from their enigmatic expression.

Shifting his gaze slightly, Paul flicked a lazy smile towards his son. 'It appears to be going well.'

Nicos made an enthusiastic response, and Stacey let her eyes wander from Paul to his son. They were so much alike, it was evident Nicos would attain the same lithe frame, the broad muscularity of his father, given a few more years. Their stance was totally similar—the easy assurance, the confidence that wealth invariably provided, as well as an inborn awareness of their own sexuality. The number of covetous and at times frankly overt glances Nicos received from the girls present made it obvious he had already achieved some of the success that Paul had enjoyed for several years with the opposite sex. With luck Nicos would be less cruel and develop a lesser degree of implacability, and therefore lack the mantle of cynicism Paul invariably adopted.

'Yes,' Nicos agreed, 'everyone seems to be enjoying themselves.' He glanced towards Stacey with a faintly appealing smile. 'Will you stay for a while? My friends think you're great.'

'The boys at any rate,' Paul returned with droll cynicism, and Stacey felt a warm tide of tell-tale colour flood her cheeks.

'It's nice of you to ask,' she managed quietly, ignoring Paul completely, 'but I promised Sophie I'd give her a hand in the kitchen.'

'After supper you must stay here,' Nicos insisted. 'Dad, you'll come, too.'

'Stacey and I will share your supper, then return for half an hour before everyone is due to leave,' said Paul with calm inflexibility, softening his words with a smile. 'If we stay, your friends will imagine we have an ulterior motive in doing so.'

'You could be right, I guess,' Nicos concurred, his gaze shifting idly round the room and lighting fractionally before turning back to them. 'If you'll excuse me—Helena is on her own. See you later, okay?'

As soon as Nicos began weaving his way towards the girl in question, Stacey moved over to the bar and deposited her empty glass, then disregarding Paul she quietly slipped from the room.

She hadn't gone more than a few steps when a hand clamped hold of her arm, and she swung round to meet Paul's sardonic gaze. At once her temper rose to the fore, and her eyes glittered angrily as she swept him a questioning glance. 'What do you want?'

One eyebrow rose in silent mockery. 'Do you really want me to answer that?'

'You're impossible!' she hissed wrathfully, and was further incensed when his mouth curved with ill-concealed cynicism.

'Because I find it—distasteful to observe my wife making an exhibition of herself among my son's friends?'

Fury exploded into violent speech. 'Exhibition? Good grief, anyone would think you were jealous!' She wrenched her arm away and began walking rapidly down the hall, only to come to an abrupt halt as he swung her round to face him.

For a moment their eyes clashed in silent antipathy, then with a husky imprecation he dragged her close, his head descending as his arms made her a prisoner against the muscular hardness of his body.

Stacey was powerless to avoid that faintly cruel mouth as it captured hers, and she gave a silent groan as he parted her lips with punishing strength. When at last he raised his head she could only look at him speechlessly for several seconds.

'Was that meant to prove something?' she said at last, and saw his eyes harden with frightening rage.

'This—war you continue to foster must inevitably reach its conclusion,' Paul declared with dangerous silkiness. 'A word of warning—when it comes to weapons, mine are in an entirely different category from yours.'

'You own temporary lease of my body,' Stacey reminded shakily, brushing a hand over her trembling lips. 'My emotions are my own.'

His mouth twisted into a humourless smile. 'Indeed?' Remembering how easily he could break down her defences and evoke a passionate response was galling, and she averted her gaze from the mockery she knew to be evident in those dark sardonic eyes above her own.

'Sophie requires my help with supper,' she said stoically, and started visibly as he took hold of her chin with hard merciless fingers.

'I have something for you in my study,' he said smoothly. 'A token of gratitude, if you like, for organising this party for Nicos.' His eyes narrowed in silent warning as she began to protest. 'You will accept it, Stacey,' he advised inflexibly. 'Nicos will be hurt if you don't.'

'Nicos chose it?'

'Yes.' His voice was clipped, and she met his gaze unflinchingly.

'In that case, I shall accept it with pleasure.'

Silently he took her arm and led her into the study, crossing behind the wide leather-topped desk to open a drawer from which he extracted a square jeweller's box. Without a word he handed it to her, and she opened it with slightly shaking fingers.

A slim bracelet nestled in a bed of white silk, twin

cords of gold twisted together to form an unusual design that was exquisite, and undoubtedly expensive.

'Thank you,' she said quietly, slipping it on to her wrist. 'It isn't necessary to give me anything.'

'Most women thrive on such trinkets,' Paul uttered wryly, and she lifted clear eyes to meet his.

'I'm not "most women",' she indicated quietly.

'No,' he acknowledged dryly. 'I am undecided whether it is genuine, or due to a superb feat of acting.'

'I feel sorry for you, Paul,' she said slowly. 'You're so cynically analytical that honest sincerity is something you fail to recognise.'

'You would have me believe you to be a veritable paragon of virtue?' he slanted sardonically. 'With a temper such as yours?'

'You provoke me—deliberately, on occasion,' she added. 'Just for the sheer hell of taking me to task.'

'You are not averse to inciting me to anger,' Paul countered with a certain degree of resignation. 'How do you expect me to react?'

Stacey glanced away from his penetrating gaze, allowing her eyes to wander idly over the bookshelves that ran floor to ceiling along an entire wall. 'The circumstances surrounding our relationship don't exactly promote a mutual empathy,' she offered slowly.

'And I am an impossible Greek, am I not?'

'Indisputably,' Stacey returned wryly, and heard his laughter.

'Whom you hate, hm?'

Did she? She wasn't sure, any more. Loath to examine her feelings in depth, she turned towards the door. 'It's after eleven,' she declared evenly. 'Sophie will be expecting my help to serve supper.' Reaching out, she grasped the doorknob and twisted it open. 'Thank you for the bracelet, it's beautiful.'

'I shall see that you do thank me—appropriately, at a more opportune time,' Paul inclined mockingly, and she escaped before he could add anything further.

In the kitchen Sophie had everything organised, so that there was very little for Stacey to do except begin loading the portable trolley with dishes of steaming food, then wheel it down the hallway.

Alex had already set up a trestle table in readiness, and a collection of assorted cutlery and enumerable paper plates were set out. Within minutes Sophie followed with yet another trolley laden with food, and together she and Stacey placed the serving dishes on the table, then stood back as Nicos and his guests converged with considerable relish to assuage their hunger.

'Can they eat that much, do you think?' Sophie queried with faint perplexity, and Stacey uttered a laugh.

'Wait and see,' she grinned. 'All that dancing works up an appetite.'

'To be young again!' the older woman sighed, and a deep voice drawled wryly from behind,

'I suggest we each take a plate and help ourselves before there is nothing left.'

The food was delectable, and ten minutes later Stacey placed her plate in the plastic container provided, then began collecting together all the emptied dishes, only to have Sophie click her tongue in silent admonishment.

'No, you must leave this to me.' She waved a hand towards the stereo which had suddenly increased in volume. 'You must enjoy yourself now. Everyone is dancing.'

'Stacey.' Nicos was at her elbow, a slow smile creasing his pleasant features. 'Will you dance with me?'

After that she scarcely kept track of the time or the number of dances she had, and it was with some surprise that she turned to find Paul at her side.

'My turn, I think,' he said, taking hold of her hand, and she tilted her head slightly, for he seemed to tower above her after being partnered by Nicos' teenage companions.

Expecting him to dance conventionally, she was surprised when he began effecting the latest disco steps, and she cast sparkling, faintly disbelieving eyes up to meet his rather wry smile.

Talking was ruled out by the loudness of the music, and when the LP on the turntable finished, someone put on a slow track and switched off the overhead lights so that only two wall-lamps glowed in soft illumination.

A few giggles and several audible groans greeted this turn of events, and Paul drew Stacey close with a slight chuckle.

'Blame Alex for that intervention,' he murmured close to her ear. 'It's a subtle hint that the evening is about to draw to a conclusion.'

Stacey didn't say anything. She was far too aware of the lithe muscular body so close to her own and the arms that held her against him. His breath stirred her hair as she rested her head on his chest, and she could have sworn the powerful heartbeat increased fractionally. His hands slid down her spine, drawing her hips firmly against him so that she was in no doubt as to his arousal, and his lips trailed a feathery path from her temple down to the edge of her mouth.

The temptation to turn slightly and meet his lips with her own was almost more than she could bear, and she whispered faintly, 'Please don't. Not here.'

For a moment she thought he might ignore her plea,

then she caught his slow smile as he loosened his hold.
'I guess I can wait until we go upstairs.'

'You'll have to,' she said breathlessly, conscious of the
surreptitious glances they were receiving, and he
uttered a soft taunting chuckle.

'You are under no illusions, eh?'

She gave a strangled reply which was met with subdued laughter, and somehow she managed to get
through the ensuing quarter of an hour as they alternatively bade Nicos' guests goodnight and politely
urged the few remaining stragglers towards the front
entrance.

It was almost two o'clock when she climbed the stairs
to their bedroom, and as Paul closed the door behind
them she stifled a prodigious yawn. Nicos' expressed
thanks had been praise enough—that, and the fact that
he had thoroughly enjoyed himself.

Her hand went to the zip fastener at the back of her
dress, then came to a sudden halt as firm fingers slid the
metal clip down beyond her waist. Slowly, one by one,
her clothes were discarded, then she was in his arms,
her mouth meeting his with a hunger that faintly
shocked her, and conscious that she no longer possessed
the will to resist his passion she submitted to the dis-
ruptive sensuality of his touch, becoming lost beneath
his undoubted expertise as he patiently transported her
into a world of tumultuous emotion.

CHAPTER NINE

STACEY stood at the window watching the steady downpour soak the neatly cut lawns. September was supposed to herald the beginning of spring, yet during
the past few weeks there had been little respite from
the rain to give credence to the approach of summer.
True, there had been intermittent bursts of sunshine
among the showers, but not sufficient to engender a
lifting of the spirit after months of cold wet weather.

There were several things she could do to occupy
the day, but none had any real appeal. The prospect
of battling the elements solely to fill in time browsing
among the shops failed to offer a necessary boost to
her morale, for there was nothing she needed.

A strange mood of introspection seemed to settle on
her slim young shoulders, and she moved them restlessly, willing the feeling to disappear. Examining and
analysing her emotions was something she had pushed
to one side, for there seemed little point in pursuing
such an exercise. Now they crowded into her brain,
forcing recognition of their existence.

Dear God, she couldn't be in love with Paul, could
she? Love didn't spring from hate, it was a gentle
emotion that grew steadily between two caring people.
Not something that alternately reached the heights,
then plunged to the depths of despair.

But if it wasn't love, what caused that prickle of
awareness whenever he entered the same room? She
could sense his presence before she saw him, and her
eyes flew straight to his, oblivious to anyone else in

154

the room. Sexually they were compatible to a degree that almost frightened her at times, and although it was becoming increasingly difficult to distinguish between love and lust, there was little doubt Paul enjoyed their lovemaking. But was it because of *her*, or would any woman suffice to satisfy his physical needs? He was an experienced lover, and surmising just how much practice he had had with innumerable women over the years brought on waves of jealousy so acute it became a tangible ache.

The large house seemed empty without Nicos' presence now that he had returned to boarding school, and after being satisfactorily employed for several years, she found having to fill in so much time was becoming tiresome. What she needed was a job.

'No,' Paul refused with terse emphasis when she broached the subject over dinner that evening.

'Why?' she demanded, her hackles rising at his adamant refusal.

'It's out of the question,' he dismissed, and she forced a laugh.

'Forgive me, Paul—I should have realised,' she said with marked sarcasm. 'You're a male chauvinist of the highest order, aren't you?'

His smile held wry cynicism. 'My wealth precludes the necessity of a working wife. If you are bored, then it is up to you to find a remedy. Take up one of the arts—painting, sculpting. Study a language, become involved in a charity organisation—my mother patronises several,' he added with an expressive shrug. 'Telephone her.'

'I don't want to sit with a group of well-endowed matrons sipping tea and dispensing largesse,' Stacey argued. 'I want to do something constructive.' She drew an encompassing arc with her arm. 'This house

is beautifully maintained, the meals are a gastronomical delight. Oh, don't you see?' she implored.
'I'm not the sort of person to drift around all day
making a production of doing nothing!'

'Plan a dinner party,' Paul suggested, and was rewarded with a speculative smile.

'I can invite anyone?'

'Check with me first in case I have something else
arranged—and yes, invite whom you please.' His brow
creased into a slight frown. 'Come to think of it, we
owe Christina a meal.'

Like a red rag to a bull, Stacey met the challenge
head-on. 'Then of course we must return her hospitality.' Her voice was sweet and polite, her brain
rapidly whirling with devious thoughts. Christina
Goulandris was in for a surprise! 'I'll ring her tomorrow,' she offered, glancing upwards and meeting
Paul's enigmatic gaze. 'Will any evening this week
be all right?'

'Yes,' he drawled. 'I promised my mother we would
drive down and have dinner one evening this week,
but I can consult her after you have confirmed a date
with Christina.'

'You're very fond of her, aren't you?'

An eyebrow rose in sardonic amusement. 'My mother,
or Christina?'

A flash of animosity lit her eyes for a brief second.
'I'm sure it's *both*,' she returned swiftly. 'But it was
your mother I was referring to.'

Paul made an impatient gesture, and his gaze became dark and penetrating. 'My father was killed in an
air-crash almost eighteen years ago. As the only son, I
am aware of her dependence upon me. We share a
deep mutual bond.'

Stacey swallowed, then broached the question that

had niggled insidiously over the past few weeks. 'Was that why you married so young?'

He was silent for so long that she thought he might not answer, and she unconsciously held her breath, aware of a tense knot of nerves in the pit of her stomach.

'If you are suggesting I married out of a sense of duty, then you are mistaken,' he said brusquely, and a shaft of pain stabbed her heart.

'I won't apologise for being curious,' she said defensively, and caught the tightening of the muscles along his jaw.

'The subject is not open for discussion,' he declared bleakly, rising to his feet. 'I have a meeting I must attend. Don't wait up for me—I'll be late.'

He strode towards the door without so much as a backward glance, and minutes later Stacey heard the muted power of the car's engine as it sped down the driveway.

There was little she could do to allay the torment his words aroused, and with determined resolve she set about planning a dinner party for a select few—namely Christina and an escort.

The invitation extended, Christina designated any of the remaining evenings in the week, and Stacey quickly confirmed it for the following day. Next, came the necessary consultation with Sophie, and the menu was planned to a fine detail.

Stacey spent the whole of Wednesday in a state of suspended animation, choosing and discarding with equal rapidity a suitable dress from the selection in her capacious wardrobe, deciding after much deliberation to wear the elegantly-cut emerald silk with its fitted waist and flowing skirt. The deep vibrant colour showed her finely-textured creamy skin to an advantage and highlighted her eyes. Slim-heeled evening sandals gave her extra height, and she fastened a tiny topaz pendant on its fine gold chain around her neck, matching it with topaz ear-studs as her only jewellery apart from the rings Paul had given her.

At six-thirty she added the final touches to her make-up and ran a brush through the length of her hair, then stood back from the mirror to scrutinise her reflection with the air of one who has done everything possible to enhance her natural attributes.

'Beautiful,' Paul drawled from the open doorway, and Stacey turned slowly, making a slight bow at his sardonically amused compliment.

'Thank you,' she acknowledged, sparing him a glance through over-bright eyes. In a dark formal evening suit and snowy white linen he looked even more dangerously formidable than usual. 'You're rather a splendid spectacle yourself.'

With long indolent strides he covered the distance between them, lifting an idle hand to her throat and fingering the delicate gold chain around her slender neck. 'I haven't seen this before. Was it a gift?'

A mischievous imp tempted her to tease him, and feigning a lack of guile Stacey lifted hazel eyes to meet his studied gaze. 'Any reason why it shouldn't be, Paul? I didn't spend the years before I met you in a convent.'

'A former admirer?' The lean fingers taunted fractionally, and heavy lids lowered to mask his expression as he appeared to examine the pendant. 'A pretty little trinket—genuine, although relatively inexpensive.' A quick tug and the chain lay broken in his hand.

Stacey clutched the faint stinging pain at the back of her neck, and her face whitened with shock. 'That was my mother's wedding gift from my father,' she whispered with incredulous horror. 'How could you?'

There was no contrition forthcoming. 'The result of your own folly in taunting me,' Paul stated hardily, and she gasped out loud.

'You savage!' she accused, her voice and temper rising to the fore. 'My God, you're detestable—I hate you!'

'Is that all?' His mouth twisted into a bitter smile. 'I am disappointed at your lack of originality.'

Never in her life had she felt so close to physical violence, and the hand she extended shook with anger. 'Give it to me!'

With an unhurried movement he slipped the chain into an inner pocket of his jacket, his eyes inscrutable as they regarded her. 'I'll ensure that it is mended,' he drawled, and Stacey turned away feeling sick and disillusioned.

'Visibly restored to its former perfection,' she voiced with intended sarcasm, her hand moving beneath the heavy swathe of her hair as she probed shaking fingers over the wounding scratch at the base of her nape.

Without warning her hair was swept aside and she cried out loud as she felt the warmth of his mouth descend on to the thin line of raw flesh. 'Don't touch me!' she vented furiously, wrenching away from him and sobbing impotently as he effortlessly held her still. Then he turned her round, and there was nothing she could do to evade those sensuous lips.

Grim determination kept her teeth firmly clenched, and seconds later he thrust her away with a muttered oath of disgust.

His expression was dark and forbidding as he raked her stormy features. 'Our guests are due to arrive soon,' he informed her ruthlessly. 'If you are not downstairs within five minutes, I will come and fetch you.'

The tone of his voice warned of the inadvisability of flouting his comand, then the bedroom door crashed shut with an intensity of sound that made her jump.

Stacey lifted shaking hands and covered her face, too numbed with shock to move. Dear heaven, how could she possibly summon sufficient control to go down and face an entire evening with him in the presence of guests—Christina Goulandris in particular! She wanted to cry and rage—achieve a release from the anger that gripped her with a force that was frightening.

Oh God, her face! Her make-up would be beyond repair and have to be re-done all over again. In a trance she crossed to the dressing-table and sank down on to the stool, her hands mechanically retrieving an assortment of jars and tubes from the deep central drawer.

The reflected image in the elegant oval mirror looked calm and composed, the eyes wide and deeply gold, the mouth full, the slightly parted lips appearing faintly swollen and totally lacking any artifice. There was little evidence of the turbulent rage that coursed her veins—only a suspicious brightness in those gold-flecked hazel eyes. Stacey drew a deep breath, then picked up a lipstick and applied colour to her lips. A few quick strokes of the brush restored her hair to its former ordered state, and with outward coolness she left the bedroom and descended the stairs.

Paul stood facing her as she entered the lounge, his rugged features an inscrutable mask. A crystal goblet half filled with amber-coloured spirits rested in one hand, the other thrust into his trouser pocket. Without a word he turned towards the drinks cabinet and filled a delicate fluted glass from a decanter, then handed it to her.

Stacey accepted it in silence, and took a few sips of the sharp fruity sherry with little regard for its excellent quality. Muted strains from a nearby stereo console filled the poignant stillness in the large room, but she scarcely heard the music, much less identified it, as she stood tensed for the sound of the front doorbell.

The melodic chimes caused her to start involuntarily, and she took an over-large gulp in the hope that the alcoholic content would inject an instant dose of spontaneity so that she could greet Christina and conduct herself with the required panache for the remainder of the evening.

Feeling like an automaton, she summoned a smile, and conscious of a light clasp at her elbow she moved forward with Paul as Sophie announced their guests.

'Darling, how marvellous to see you again!' Christina greeted brightly, her eyes devouring Paul as she moved into the room.

'Christina, Spiros,' Paul acknowledged with urbanity. 'A drink—what can I offer you?'

'I'll have my usual, darling,' Christina responded, affording Stacey the minimal courtesy as she drifted after Paul's lithe frame, and Stacey turned politely towards Spiros, engaging him in meaningless conversation until Paul had performed his duty as a host.

'I adore your dress,' Christina drawled, detecting its designer label and assessing its cost in one upward sweep of her falsely layered lashes. 'So slim, my sweet,' she continued with feigned envy. 'You must tell me your dieting secrets. Not that I need to worry overmuch,' she added with malicious satisfaction.

No, Stacey agreed silently, not now, but in a few years those voluptuous curves will run to undisguised fat if you're not careful. Out loud she said sweetly, 'I don't diet, Christina. I enjoy my food.'

'Really? One would not have thought so from the bird-like portions you consumed in my apartment several weeks ago.'

Bitch, Stacey replied, 'I prefer to tread gently with rich spicy dishes that I've not previously sampled. If you remember, Paul and I had been married less than a week, and at that stage Greek food was unfamiliar to me.'

'And now, Stacey?' the other arched coyly. 'Are you familiar with everything Greek?'

With considerable calm she responded evenly, 'That's something you'll have to ask Paul.'

Dark eyes swept from one to the other with quizzical amusement. 'As a wife Stacey meets all my require-ments,' he endorsed lightly, lifting his glass to his lips in a silent eloquent toast, and Christina cast him a faintly reproachful glance.

'I thought only Eleni was capable of that, my dear.'

Paul lifted one eyebrow in silent reproof. 'If that were true, I would not have remarried,' he slanted with aloof imperturbability, and Christina had the grace to look faintly chastened.

It was a relief when Sophie announced dinner, and Stacey entered the formal dining-room with a sense of anticipated elation. From the damask cloth on the table to the fine china, the polished silverware and the assortment of crystal, the setting couldn't be faulted.

As soon as they were seated, Sophie wheeled in the portable serving trolley and proceeded to serve the first course. A selection of two dishes for each course had been planned, and as an appetiser there was a choice of octopus in vinegar, *htapodi xydato*; or vine leaves stuffed with rice, *dolmathakia yalantzi*.

To follow there was shrimp soup, *garidosoupa*; and the main course consisted of stuffed squid, *calamarakia yemista*; meat on skewers, *souvlaka*; and pilaf with mussels, *mydia pilafi*. Dessert consisted of Greek pancakes, *tyganites*, and preserved cherries, *glyko kerasi*.

It was an hour before Greek coffee was served, but it took less than fifteen minutes for Stacey to realise that Christina was aware that the menu had been deliberately planned. Not only was it deliberately planned, but Stacey had made a point of choosing seafood, not only mussels, but squid and octopus. True, her portions were small, but sufficient to denote enjoyment to the casual onlooker—who, at that table, could only have been Spiros!

Conversation throughout had concentrated upon the usual pleasantries exchanged on such occasions, and any barbs Christina thrust Stacey was able to fend with apparent ease.

Paul was an attentive host and an equally attentive husband—almost too much so, much to Stacey's chagrin. His eyes, whenever she caught those jet orbs cast in her direction, were warm and faintly speculative, and more than once they held the promise of passion, the intimate gleam given by one lover to another. He rarely touched her, for he was much too subtle for that, but his lusty regard was clearly evident, as he meant it to be, and she seethed inwardly, praying for the evening to conclude so that she could give vent to the indisputable rage being stoked towards its ultimate eruption with every glance, every word from the shamelessly unprincipled man who had coerced her into marriage.

At last they were alone, and as the car slid away from the front entrance down the driveway Stacey moved back from the doorway, waiting only until the door was firmly shut behind their departing guests before bursting into furious speech.

'You're totally, irrepressibly impossible!' she hissed witheringly, becoming even more incensed as she glimpsed his cynical amusement.

'Indeed? I thought my manner exemplary,' he declared dryly.

'My God!' Words temporarily failed her. 'You behaved like a—a lusty animal!'

His eyes narrowed slightly and became hooded. 'Would you rather I had made it evident that we were at odds with each other?'

'No,' she allowed. 'But there was no need to act as if you could hardly wait to get me into bed!'

'Your delectable body is a source of constant fascination to me,' he drawled, and she hurled wrathfully,

'I possess a brain, too! How do you think I feel every time you make use of me?'

'What about your heart?' he parried mockingly. 'Is it not often at war with your brain? Deny if you dare the joy you derive in my arms.'

'You're a primitive savage, Paul. I count the days until I can be free of you!'

'And the nights?'

Her eyes flashed explosively. 'I can never win an argument, can I?'

'If it matters so much, I daresay I could be persuaded to allow you to think you get the better of me on occasion.'

'How magnanimous of you! Save it for some other poor woman who enjoys being beneath a man's thumb. Thumb!' she derided. 'Dear lord, beneath your *foot* is a more appropriate expression! You belong back in the Dark Ages when man was king and his woman little more than a servant.'

'All evening you have been spoiling for a fight, hm?

Revenge for the grievance you are harbouring, isn't that so?'

'Yes—damn you!'

'Then fight me. But be warned that I intend utilising some measure of defence,' he drawled sardonically.

To admit defeat was something she would not tolerate. 'It was unforgivable,' she reiterated. 'Even if the necklace had been a gift from a former friend, you had no right to tear it from my neck with such disregard.'

'You are my wife,' Paul asserted silkily. 'I can well afford to give you any jewellery you desire. Replace if necessary any item you already own. I will not permit you to retain gifts from other men, is that understood?'

'Do you require a full confession of all my sins?' she demanded tautly. 'A few furtive kisses, the unmemorable skirmishes after an infrequent date? I was too busy being mother and father to Trisha and earning a living to indulge in frivolous games.' She lifted her head to gaze at him defiantly. 'What if I were to demand you discard all the gifts your innumerable women have heaped upon your head?'

'Boxed monogrammed handkerchiefs, an exclusive designer tie, the occasional pair of cuff-links?' An eyebrow arched quizzically. 'It was *I* who despatched the gifts—payment for favours received,' he added cynically.

The anger drained out of her, leaving sickening emptiness in its place as she imagined just how many women there had been. 'I'm tired,' she evinced with a weariness that wasn't feigned, and uttered a stifled gasp as she felt her feet leave the floor. 'Put me down!'

At the dark penetrating look he slanted her she began to struggle, then as he began mounting the stairs she allowed her head to droop against his shoulder. 'No, Paul, don't—not tonight, I couldn't bear it.'

At the edge of the bed when he set her down on to her feet, she made one last effort. 'Please——' Anything else she might have uttered was lost as his mouth met hers with lazy deliberation, the seducing quality of his lips igniting the sleeping flame deep within, and she gave a moan of despair.

His hands were freeing the zip fastening at the back of her dress, and he lifted his mouth fractionally. 'Stop me, Stacey,' he murmured huskily. 'Another few seconds and I will allow no retraction.'

Oh God, she groaned, why did her body respond to his touch as a separate entity from her brain? How fickle was the demands of the flesh! She wanted him desperately, and foolish pride had no place as she lifted her arms to clasp his dark head to hers.

She met his mouth with a hunger that sent waves of self-disgust washing over her, then she was beyond caring as he matched and surpassed her desire, bringing her yet again to the brink of ecstasy.

Afterwards there was time for self-recrimination, and she fell asleep with the stain of tears on her cheeks, the knowledge that her love was utterly hopeless and lay like a heavy load upon her slender shoulders.

It was a week later that Stacey left the house shortly after nine with the intention of spending most of the day browsing among the many boutiques in the inner city. It would have been more enjoyable to have had company, but all of her friends worked, and she was still too wary of Paul's mother to suggest Mrs Leandros accompany her.

Nearing the end of September, the air was still cold, but the sun when it did condescend to shine for any length of time was gradually gaining more strength, and the promise of spring could be evidenced on the branches of the trees that lined Melbourne's city and suburban streets.

The noisy clacking of the trams as they sped along their steel tracks and the constant sound of traffic rang in Stacey's ears as she wandered along Bourke Street.

By midday she had a sizeable collection of assorted packages, and her feet in their fashionable boots were beginning to ache. The need for a brief rest combined with the more basic necessity for food and coffee sent her into the nearest coffee lounge.

After that the time simply flew, and it was almost three o'clock when, passing a shop window, the sight of a leather handbag drew Stacey into the shop for a closer inspection. It was the colour she wanted to go with some new shoes she had purchased earlier that morning, and it took only a few minutes to decide on the purchase.

Emerging from the shop, she accidentally brushed against a passer-by, and she turned, an apology on her lips, and saw to her dismay that it was Christina Goulandris.

'Hello there.' Christina's smile was brilliant as she spared Stacey a swift raking glance. 'Shopping?'

'I've finished,' she answered politely, and the other girl's smile widened.

'Spending Paul's money, I see.'

'My own, actually,' Stacey responded, loath to stand there parrying words with someone she had little time for.

'Marrying Paul was quite a *coup* for you, wasn't it, darling?' Christina began sweetly. 'A plutocrat who is all man.' She uttered a light laugh, her eyes suddenly vicious. 'But then you know that, don't you? He's quite something—attuned to a woman's needs as a master fiddler to a Stradivarius.' She tilted her head slightly, regarding Stacey with mockery. 'Doesn't it bother you he has known so many women?'

Stacey forced a smile to her lips. 'Should it?'

'My dear, aren't you concerned about his fidelity? When a man has had his pick of all the exotic fruits, it isn't possible he can be content with only an apple for very long—and a green one, at that,' Christina added with thinly-veiled cruelty.

'You know what they say about apples,' Stacey declared her eyes deliberately guileless. 'As well as one a day keeping the doctor away, the *green* ones are crunchy-crisp and juicy—so refreshing after a surfeit of rich tropical fruits that tend to be a mite overripe.'

Christina's eyes flashed with vicious enmity. 'My, my, you do possess a sharp tongue!'

'I can pay you a similar compliment.'

'You're looking a trifle peaky, my dear. Pale, all eyes, and I'll swear you've lost weight. Are you by any chance pregnant?' Dark eyes stabbed Stacey's slender frame, then returned remorselessly. 'My poor sweet, imagine how cumbersome you'll look in a few months' time!' She moved fractionally, weighing her words for their utmost effect. 'I'll be waiting to take up with Paul where we left off before you came along. I have no scruples where he is concerned, you see.'

Stacey felt the rage inside her rise rapidly to the surface, and she knew she had to get away, fast—or erupt! 'Good luck, Christina,' she bade with apparent unconcern. 'I really must go. You will forgive me if I say that meeting you hasn't been a pleasure?' she concluded coolly, and prepared to sidestep so that she could continue through the arcade to the main street.

'Paul has an engraved gold-plated key to my apartment,' Christina informed her as a parting thrust, and Stacey was unable to resist taunting,

'Really? How—desperate of you.' Without a backward glance she began walking, and was unprepared for the vicious shove that sent her lunging forward on to her knees. Parcels cascaded all around her, and she was too stunned to move for several seconds, until the solicitous help of a passer-by brought her shakily to her feet.

Dear God, it didn't bear thinking about! Such bitter acrimony, and in public, too. Stacey murmured her thanks as the parcels were gathered together, and she reassured the kindly matron that she was fine—just fine.

For a moment she couldn't even remember where she had parked the car, for her brain seemed temporarily numb, and it took several seconds before she felt calm enough to think clearly.

Driving home Stacey took time to reflect, blaming Christina's hurtful barbs for magnifying niggling doubt into open speculation. There was evidence of too many symptoms for them to be ignored, and medical confirmation was highly recommended. If Christina noticed, then it wouldn't be long before others did. And Paul? How long could she hope to hide it from him? He knew every curve of her body in intimate detail—a thickening waistline couldn't be disguised as a weight-gain in an otherwise increasingly slender frame.

Almost without conscious thought Stacey drove to the doctor's surgery where she had been a patient for as long as she could remember, and made immediate arrangements for the necessary tests to be undertaken in a nearby clinic.

It was after five when she arrived home, and she

barely had time to unpack her purchases before Paul entered their room.

'Shopping?'

Stacey spared him a quick glance before returning to the task at hand. 'Yes.' She crossed to her capacious clothes closet and took out two spare hangers.

'You look—nettled,' he drawled, and she snapped, 'I'm perfectly fine.'

'Indeed?'

'Stop it, Paul,' she said wearily, returning to the bed and sliding a dress on to a hanger. Her nerve-ends tingled with awareness as he moved towards her, and she felt her stomach give a sickening jolt as his lips brushed against the vulnerable hollow at the edge of her nape.

'Hm,' he murmured musingly. 'This perfume is delightful. Guerlain, is it not?'

'You should know,' Stacey threw with a touch of petulance, and he gave a throaty laugh.

'Stacey, such a loaded comment demands an explanation.'

She twisted away from him, only to be brought back again and she winced against the biting strength of his hands.

'Careful,' he warned implacably. 'You bristle with indignation, rather like a cross little kitten—all claws and tiny sharp teeth. What happened today?' he demanded softly.

She drew in a deep breath, willing control over her turbulent emotions. 'The perfume is Chamade,' she informed him calmly, then gave a painful gasp as his grip tightened. 'You're hurting me!'

'I will hurt you even more if you don't tell me what I want to know.'

'Christina and I ran into each other,' she capitulated, aware of his fingers effecting a probing massage where only seconds before they had bruised her flesh.

'And?'

'She made certain comments to which I took exception.'

'Such as?'

Stacey cast him a bitter glance. 'I'm sure you're able to use your imagination! Your affairs seem to be without number!'

'Poor Stacey, are you jealous?'

'Of course not,' she denied quickly. 'I dislike being humiliated, that's all.'

A slight frown creased his brow, and his eyes narrowed fractionally. 'Christina humiliated you?'

She gave a sigh that defied description. 'Leave it, Paul. I'm quite able to stand up for myself.'

He leant out a hand and lifted her chin, regarding her with an intentness that was disquieting. 'Christina and I are old friends.'

'So she took pleasure in informing me,' Stacey snapped, veiling her eyes to hide the flicker of pain that engulfed her momentarily, then regaining control she allowed them to sweep upwards to meet his unflinchingly. 'I presume you've handed back the gold-plated key to her apartment—or perhaps you still have it?'

For an instant his dark eyes held a speculative gleam, then it was gone. 'I never had a key. When I entertain a woman, it is at a place of my choosing.'

'Of course,' she acknowledged with a tinge of bitterness. 'Wealthy jet-set playboys have an apartment, a penthouse suite, as well as a home at their disposal. Then there are an endless selection of motels.'

'I will admit I've had my share, but if I had conducted as many affairs as you suggest, I would scarcely have had time to succeed in the business world,' Paul declared dryly.

'Is that a statement or a confession?'

'Neither. I am answerable to no one.'

'Not even to your wife?' Stacey parried.

'You are in no position to bargain,' he taunted softly, and she wrenched herself out of his grasp.

'I want to shower and change for dinner.' With shaking fingers she collected clean underwear and a velour wrap, then crossed to the bathroom without so much as a backward glance.

Dinner was a strained affair with Paul choosing to eat in comparative silence, and Stacey unwilling to contribute anything at all left the table at the end of the meal having said not so much as a word. Her appetite was negligible to the point of being non-existent, and as each course was cleared and another brought she offered an apologetic glance in the hope that it would appease Sophie. It didn't, and she was left with the feeling that everything, and everyone, was against her.

It was something of a relief when Paul informed her of his intention to closet himself in the study for the rest of the evening, and she escaped downstairs to play some tapes on Nicos' stereo. Usually it was easy to lose herself in the music, allowing it to seep into her brain until it wiped out conscious thought, but tonight too many things crowded for supremacy—foremost being her possible pregnancy.

Tomorrow she would know for certain. But that was hours away—seventeen, to be exact. How on earth could she manage to get through them? she tormented herself restlessly.

Unable to settle, she stood to her feet and switched off the console, then moved to the television, watching the flickering images fleetingly before changing channels and ultimately turning it off. Perhaps a book would engage her interest sufficiently so that she might immerse herself entirely, and with feverish intention she searched the bookshelves, selecting several titles at random until she had piled no less than six into her arms.

Bed and a good book for an avid reader was the panacea for all ills, but tonight Stacey was denied even that, and after an hour spent sightlessly turning pages she thrust the pile of books down on to the floor, then reached for the bed-lamp to extinguish the light.

Sleep remained an elusive shadowy entity which she constantly strived to capture, and long after Paul had joined her she lay staring up at the ceiling, her thoughts too jumbled to assemble into rational order.

CHAPTER TEN

STACEY registered the faint ting of the receiver as she replaced it, and the anxiety of the past few weeks climaxed in one horrifying crescendo, forcing realisation of her predicament. In today's world there was no excuse for ignorance regarding contraceptive measures, so why hadn't she attended to it? Dear God, it seemed impossible that she had been so *blind*!

The thoughts she had hitherto pushed to the back of her mind came racing to the fore. What choice had she now, for heaven's sake?

Paul. How long could she stay without him becoming aware of his unborn child's presence—a month, two at most? Then what? At the end of her two-year term the child would be fourteen months old. Not even in her wildest imagination could she suppose Paul would let her take the child—yet how could she bear to leave it behind? The alternative, that of seeking an abortion, occurred fleetingly, only to be discarded.

A long shuddering sigh raked her body. There was only one way, and that was to leave before Paul gained the slightest glimmering of knowledge. The sooner the better.

Slowly she mounted the stairs to the bedroom, and into a suitcase she flung clothes at random, careful to pack only those which she had arrived with—was it only two months ago?

As she packed, a plan formed in her mind. She would take the car and drive straight to the airport and board the first available flight—anywhere, as long as it was away from here.

A note, just a few crucial lines on a sheet of note-paper which she propped up against the mirror of her dressing-table, then with one last glance around the elegantly furnished room she picked up her suitcase and made her way downstairs.

'Stacey, are you going out?'

Consternation, guilt, and sheer fear were quickly masked. 'Nicos! What are you doing at home?' Stacey slowed to a halt beside the front door, and endeavoured to instil some warmth into her voice. 'I thought you weren't due home until this evening,' she managed with a light laugh.

Nicos' eyes flashed from her suitcase to her expressive features. 'The sports were cancelled,' he explained carefully. 'A phone call to Dad confirmed that I had his permission to get a taxi home, rather than hang around until this evening.' His eyes clouded with faint anxiety. 'What's up, Stacey? Where are you going?'

Oh God, was she that transparent? 'This, you mean?' She held the suitcase up, and smiled. 'Just a few cast-offs for charity. I've had a springcleaning session,' she invented, pleased at how plausible it sounded. 'I was just on my way to leave them at the appropriate depot.'

His features relaxed. 'Okay. Mind if I come along for the ride?'

'I'll be a while, Nicos. I have some shopping to do as well,' she said with regret, shaking her head slowly.

He gave a light shrug, his eyes unconsciously questioning. 'See you later, then?'

'Yes,' she answered ambiguously, trying to give a re-assuring smile. Summoning forth every ounce of courage she took the few necessary steps towards the door and opened it, then moving outside she walked quickly round the side of the house to the garage.

She needed somewhere quiet where she could assemble her tangled emotions into a rational whole. Hopping on to a plane wasn't the immediate answer. She had to plan ahead, and carefully, covering her tracks so that Paul would be unable to discover her whereabouts. For that she needed time.

It struck her with sudden inspiration that Bellarine was little more than an hour away, and it would be the last place Paul would think of looking for her. Obtaining a key to the beach house was simple, for there was one among the set of keys Paul had given her within the first few weeks of their marriage.

With her destination settled, Stacey set the small car in the direction of the Prince's Highway, and on reaching it drove at maximum speed in the need to isolate herself from Paul. Exactly how he would react when he found her gone was something to which she daren't give much thought. And Nicos—he was more like a younger brother, and deserting him gave her more than a few pangs of conscience.

Stacey had little recollection of the drive to Bellarine, for her actions behind the wheel were conducted automatically and it was perhaps as well nothing untoward occurred that required an instantaneous reaction.

The wind was fierce, gusting in from the sea mingling salt-spray with the fleeting rain. Stacey turned into the driveway and brought the car to a halt beside the garage, then spent a harassing few minutes selecting the correct key to fit the folding garage doors.

The car safely under shelter, she took her suitcase from off the back seat, then she emerged from the garage and made her way towards the beach house.

It was bitterly cold, and Stacey welcomed refuge from the icy wind as she closed the front door behind her. The house was exactly as they had left it a few weeks before, except there was evidence of dust on the surface of the furniture.

Rather wearily she took her suitcase through to one of the bedrooms, choosing without conscious thought the bedroom at the rear of the house, for to have countenanced sleeping in the room she had shared with Paul was unconscionable.

Rubbing her arms with the cold, she went in search of the switch that would trip the central heating, returning after several minutes defeated. There was a fireplace in the lounge, but she had no idea whether it was in working order, or even if there was any available firewood.

A cup of coffee would be beneficial, and as she set about heating the water in the kitchen she felt the pangs of hunger gnaw her stomach, making her aware that she had eaten little since breakfast that morning. Come to think of it, she was downright hungry!

After scrambled eggs on toast she felt considerably better, and she settled into a comfortable chair with a mug of hot sweetened coffee to watch television. Not that it was very successful, for she found it impossible to concentrate on the small screen, and after an hour she simply switched it off and sat in contemplative silence.

The shrill insistent summons of the telephone made her jump with fright, and she half-rose from the chair to answer it before sinking back to listen until the dual peals ceased.

Paul, Stacey deduced. Had he read her note yet? She glanced at her watch and saw that it was after eight. He would have been home for an hour and a half. What would he have done in that time? Had dinner, contacted Trisha, perhaps—then what? It seemed inconceivable he would simply accept her desertion, but what steps would he take? The police—no, she discounted quickly. A private detective, perhaps. How long would it take before she was found?

Stacey's brain whirled with conflicting plans. Tomorrow she would catch a bus into the township, then connect with a bus back to Melbourne, and from Flinders Station she would get a train to Adelaide, then a plane to Sydney. From the anonymity of that teeming metropolis she would gain some breathing space to plan her future and that of her unborn child. Possibly the ultimate answer would be to travel across the Tasman to New Zealand and settle in Auckland, reverting back to her maiden name.

Dear lord, she was tired! It had been quite a day, one way and another, and she felt weary almost beyond measure. However, the thought of preparing for bed didn't appeal, and with a sigh she collected a blanket from the linen cupboard then crossed to one of the large sofas, and picking up a cushion she plumped it against the armrest and lay down. Perhaps she could doze for an hour or two, then she would slip into bed.

Sleep wasn't a merciful escape, for her subconscious mind whirled with an unwelcome collection of incidents that had occurred since her marriage—like a kaleidoscope over which she had no control, and she moaned out loud as she heard Paul call her name, tossing restlessly in an effort to be rid of the dark forceful figure that rose to taunt her.

'No, I won't! You can't make me!'

Stacey came to with a start, her lips parted, the sound of her own anguished voice ringing vividly in her ears. Had she actually cried out—was that what had woken her? She blinked slowly at first, then rapidly in an attempt to clear her tortured vision, for the figure of a man stood in the open doorway, and her mouth parted soundlessly.

'Paul?' Dear God, was she hallucinating? No image could portray such compelling intensity, and she struggled into a sitting position, her eyes widening with stunned comprehension. 'How did you know I was here?' she whispered in a voice that was husky with sleep.

It was impossible to discern anything from his expression, and nervousness sent her tongue edging a tantalising path across her lower lip, and she caught the soft inner tissue between her teeth in an unconscious gesture as she waited for him to speak.

'A process of elimination.' His voice was dry and tinged with faint weariness.

The silence lengthened until she could have screamed. 'The phone rang earlier—was that you?'

His answering nod confirmed her suspicion. 'Having decided to run away, it wasn't likely you would answer, even if you were here. I decided to make sure by contacting a friend who lives close by.'

It was so simple Stacey almost burst into hysterical laughter. So much for her carefully-laid plans!

'I meant what I said, Paul,' she determined slowly, meeting his steady gaze.

'Your brief note?' He arched an eyebrow, and walked slowly towards the sofa to halt less than a foot away. 'Knowing what manner of man I am, did you imagine I would let you disappear out of sight?'

'If exacting full measure is so important, I'll pay you,' she said stoically. 'Even if it takes forever.' She looked up at him carefully. 'But I'm not coming back.'

'The terms of our—arrangement,' Paul said quietly. 'They were for two years, remember?'

A clutch of fear gripped her stomach with painful intensity. 'That was a verbal agreement,' she resolved. 'I'm not sure how it would stand up in a court of law.'

'I can command the best legal brains. Can you do the same?' he queried with silky detachment, and a helpless rage brought her to her feet.

'Do your damnedest, Paul,' she declared unsteadily, and made to move past him. 'I really don't care any more.'

A hand caught hold of her arm. 'Not even if I asked you to come back—for Nicos' sake?'

Her eyes ached with suppressed emotion that pride forbade be released in anything so mortifying as tears. 'Your son is a sensible, fair-minded young man, Paul,' she said. 'I'm sure he'll understand when you explain.'

'What should I explain, Stacey?'

'I'll get my suitcase,' she said rigidly. 'It shouldn't be difficult for me to book into a hotel.'

There was a long silence that seemed to stretch into eternity, and Stacey stood immobile, her brain registering the scene like something out of a tableau.

'You will stay here,' Paul determined at last, and she tilted her chin, seeing with puzzlement that his eyes were dark with something she could have sworn was pain.

'I want nothing from you,' she said slowly, 'except a divorce. I'll sign whatever papers are necessary exonerating you from any payment for my—what is the legal term? Support?'

'What if I don't agree?'

'If you arrange payment of any money, I won't touch it!' she cried wretchedly.

'There will be no divorce, Stacey,' he stated with terse implacability, and she wrenched her arm impotently in an effort to free herself from his grasp.

'I won't stay with you,' she said desperately. 'I can't.'
Too late she realised she had actually uttered those
last two damning words, and she prayed he wouldn't
notice.

'Why—*can't*?'

'I won't stay,' Stacey rushed quickly, not quite meeting those penetrating dark eyes.

'There is a distinction between "can't" and "will
not",' Paul insisted, and she shook her head.

'Words,' she discounted. 'In the heat of anger——'
A silent gasp of pain caught in her throat as his fingers
bit into her arm. 'Paul, you're hurting me!'

'Stacey, are you expecting my child?'

It was on the tip of her tongue to deny it. '*Yes*, damn
you!' she cried in anguish, her eyes alive with fury.
'Does it please you to know I'm carrying proof of your
virility, Paul?'

'Is that why you left?' he demanded. 'Dammit,
Stacey—answer me!'

She looked up at him wordlessly. 'I'm seven weeks
pregnant. I feel sick in the morning, and I can't bear
anything tight around my waist. How long before you
would notice? Another week—maybe two?'

'Rather than tell me, you ran away,' Paul concluded
hardily. 'What was to follow—an abortion?'

'*No!*' The denial was torn from her throat.

'Then *what*?' he demanded savagely. 'Adoption?'

'How could I do that?' Stacey asked fiercely. Frus-
trated tears blurred her vision. 'You were never intended to know of its existence.' She couldn't even see
his face for the watery mist. 'There isn't a price you
can pay to persuade me to part with it,' she ended
shakily.

His face paled, the muscles tautening his features
into an expressionless mask. 'Any court of law would

grant me custody,' he informed her harshly, 'on the grounds that I can provide for its needs far more adequately than you ever could as a solo parent.'

A black void threatened to engulf her. 'You'd fight me? Dear God,' she choked, 'how you must hate me!'

'I want you to stay.'

Stacey fought to hold on to the slender thread that separated her from unconsciousness. 'How could I trust you? After the baby is born, you'll never let me take it and leave.' Tears rolled down her cheeks to slip unheeded from the edge of her chin.

'Why do you think I came after you?' Paul demanded bleakly.

'To ensure that I returned in order to fulfil the remaining twenty-one and a half months,' she answered, brushing a shaky hand over her cheeks. 'What other reason could there be?'

'Do you imagine I care about a few thousand dollars?' he declared with brooding intolerance.

'*Several* thousand dollars,' Stacey corrected, and he uttered a harsh laugh.

'Not for a hundred times that amount could I be persuaded to rush into marriage,' he declared.

She looked at him carefully, unable to control the way her heart lurched as a tiny seed of hope took root. 'What do you mean?'

'You walked into my office, accused me of having an affair with your sister, insulted me, and slapped my face—all within the space of a few minutes,' he recounted ruminatively. 'You fascinated and infuriated me, both at the same time.'

'Paul——'

'Cynical, and thoroughly sceptical where women were concerned,' he continued, his eyes holding hers with an unwavering scrutiny. 'Yet I fell in love,' he revealed slowly. 'To the extent that I was prepared to go to any lengths to make you mine—even marriage.' He gave a hollow laugh. 'Something I had never had to offer in the past.'

'But you hated me,' Stacey burst out, completely perplexed.

'Anger—at times, inimical rage,' Paul disclosed with a wry smile. 'Never hate.'

Her mouth parted, then closed again. 'Why didn't you tell me?'

'I imagined I had—with my lips, my body, every time I made love to you.'

'I thought that was just your vast—experience.'

'And an insatiable appetite?' he mocked lightly.

A blush tinged her cheeks. 'Yes,' she admitted, unable to drag her eyes away from his.

'You were too inexperienced to know the difference,' Paul taunted gently.

'You love me?' Stacey whispered incredulously, her heart stretching its wings tentatively in preparation for flight.

'Oh yes,' he declared softly. 'To the point whereby I become incensed with jealousy every time you so much as look at another man—even my own son.'

'*Nicos?*'

'Yes—*dammit*!' he swore huskily, and she smiled, her eyes lighting with mischievous laughter.

'Oh, Paul,' she teased. 'Nicos is charming and thoroughly delightful company—I'm very fond of him.'

'And his father?'

She sobered quickly. 'I think you know the answer to that.'

'Yet you left.' There was naked pain in his voice and she sought to alleviate it.

'I thought I had two years,' she explained quietly.

'In that time anything was possible—even that you might come to love me.' She searched his face, willing him to understand. 'Can you imagine how I felt when I discovered I was pregnant? If I stayed, how could I leave at the end of two years without our child—the one thing that was truly yours, and mine? To leave before you knew of its existence seemed the only thing I could do. At least then I would have something to remember you by,' she finished slowly.

'I nearly went out of my mind when I read your pitiful little note,' he growled, letting his hands slide up to her shoulders. 'I telephoned everyone I could think of—all the time desperately afraid you had taken a flight out of the city. Finding you then would have taken time—too much time,' he revealed emotively, then he swore briefly—a string of unintelligible oaths in his own language. 'You'll never have reason to want to leave me again,' he vowed, his eyes darkening as she turned her head and gently placed her lips against his hand.

Then she was in his arms, held as if he couldn't bear to let her go, and his mouth met hers with a hunger that set her heart soaring heavenwards.

'Paul?'

'Hm?' His voice was a muffled murmur as he gently teased the pulsing cord at the side of her neck.

'Can I ask you something?'

At the tentative uncertainty in her voice he lifted his head and met her gaze.

'Eleni?' he countered gently, and she nodded silently.

'If you'd rather not talk about it——'

'She was very young, barely eighteen,' Paul interrupted softly, 'and I was just two years older. We both came from wealthy families—Greek immigrants who had worked hard to build up a flourishing company.

A joint one. As she was an only child, it was important Eleni marry a fellow Greek who would maintain the company. Who better than me?' He gave a light shrug. 'We were fond of each other, it was a good match, and the company was kept in the family.' His eyes held hers. 'I had tremendous affection for her, and when she died so soon after Nicos' birth, I was devastated that someone so young and full of the joy of living should be taken. I threw myself into my work, and devoted every other waking hour to the wellbeing of my son.' He shook her gently. 'There have been women—I can't deny it. But none that I have wanted to marry—until you.' He gave a throaty laugh and bent to kiss her. 'You, I love—so much so, I ache just to look at you.'

'I'm aware of it,' Stacey teased provocatively.

'Are you, indeed?' His eyes lit with devilish laughter. 'What do you suggest we do about it?'

'We could drive back to Melbourne,' she declared, tilting her head to one side. 'On the other hand, it's quite late. We could stay here and drive back tomorrow.'

'Minx,' he declared. 'I have no intention of driving back tonight.'

'No?'

His answering smile did strange things to her equilibrium, and when he swung her into his arms she buried her face against his neck.

'You're my life,' she whispered softly. 'I think I loved you almost from the very beginning, except I couldn't recognise the emotion and fought like anything against it.'

Paul lowered her gently down to her feet beside the bed, and his hands shook slightly as they cupped her face. 'No more fighting?'

'Oh—maybe sometimes,' she conceded quizzically. 'Whenever you become totally impossible.'

'Really? And if the reverse is so?'

'I'll allow you to mete out just punishment,' she twinkled impishly, then gave a startled yelp as he drew her close and proceeded to kiss her until she was starry-eyed and breathless.

'Now the many misunderstandings are behind us,' Paul said gently. 'Only happiness lies ahead.'

'If you say so,' she said demurely.

'I do,' he declared deeply. 'I intend devoting the rest of my life proving it to you.'

Doctor Nurse Romances

and January's
stories of romantic relationships behind the scenes
of modern medical life are:

THE ICEBERG ROSE
by Sarah Franklin

Looking after the glamorous actress Romaine Hart
during her stay in a Swiss clinic seemed the ideal way
for Leane to regain confidence in her own nursing
ability. And so it might have been, but for Doctor
Adam Blake's constant interference. Why wouldn't
he leave her alone?

THE GEMEL RING
by Betty Neels

Charity disliked and despised Everard van Tijlen,
the eminent Dutch surgeon whose fees were so
outrageously expensive. Then she found herself working
with him — and her ideas began to change!

Order your copies today from your local paperback retailer

Masquerade
Historical Romances

Intrigue
excitement
romance

LYSANDER'S LADY
by Patricia Ormsby

The Polite World looked askance at Miss Katherine Honeywell, despite her beauty and fortune, when she insisted upon championing a social outcast. How unfortunate that she should have fallen in love with that arbiter of good taste, Mr Lysander Derwent!

CASTLE OF THE MIST
by Valentina Luellen

After her scandalous marriage to an impotent, elderly roué — undertaken to pay her brother's gambling debts — Isabel de Riché returned to Scotland with her reputation in shreds. And James MacLeod evidently believed every word . . .

Look out for these titles in your local paperback shop from
9th January 1981

The Mills & Boon Rose is the Rose of Romance

TEMPLE OF FIRE *by Margaret Way*
Julian Stanford had everything except a heart. Could Fleur possibly stand up to him and his overwhelming family?

ONE BRIEF SWEET HOUR *by Jane Arbor*
If Dale Ransome still chose to think the worst of Lauren, let him. She just didn't care any more — did she?

WHEN MAY FOLLOWS *by Betty Neels*
Had Katrina been incredibly foolish to want to change her life by marrying Professor Raf van Tellerinck?

LIVING TOGETHER *by Carole Mortimer*
The attractive Leon Masters was determined to get through the ice that enclosed Helen — but was his method the right one?

SEDUCTION *by Charlotte Lamb*
Clea wasn't too enthusiastic about her arranged marriage to Ben Winter, until he came along to turn her feelings upside down . . .

A GIRL POSSESSED *by Violet Winspear*
Was Janie a good enough actress to conceal her love for Pagan Pentrevah, and pretend to be married to him to keep his ex-wife at bay?

THE SUGAR DRAGON *by Victoria Gordon*
The forceful Con Bradley was quite enough for Verna to cope with, even before Madeline Cunningham arrived, with wedding bells in mind!

NEVER COUNT TOMORROW *by Daphne Clair*
Lin fell in love with Soren Wingard and everything crashed about her in ruins. Could she get away from him before she did any more harm?

ICEBERG *by Robyn Donald*
What heart Justin Doyle had belonged to his dead wife Alison. Hadn't Linnet better leave Justin to her sister Bronwyn?

AN ISLAND LOVING *by Jan MacLean*
All Kristin knew was that he brought her more happiness — and bitter unhappiness — than she had ever known. Would she ever be free of him again?

If you have difficulty in obtaining any of these books from your local paperback retailer, write to:

Mills & Boon Reader Service
P.O. Box 236, Thornton Road, Croydon, Surrey; CR9 3RU.
Available February 1981

A new idea in romance for Mothers Day

Mothers Day is Sunday March 29th. This year, for the first time ever, there's a special Mills & Boon Mothers Day Gift Pack.* Best Seller Romances by favourite authors are presented in this attractive gift pack. The pack costs no more than if you buy the four romances individually.

It is a lovely gift idea for Mothers Day. Every mother enjoys romance in reading.

DANGEROUS MASQUERADE
Janet Dailey

TO BUY A BRIDE
Roberta Leigh

BEWARE THE BEAST
Anne Mather

THE CHILD OF JUDAS
Violet Winspear.

*Available in UK from Feb. 13th

£3.00

The rose of romance
Mills & Boon

CUT OUT AND POST THIS PAGE TO RECEIVE

FREE *FULL COLOUR* Mills & Boon CATALOGUE

and – if you wish – why not also ORDER NOW any (or all) of the favourite titles offered overleaf?

Because you've enjoyed *this* Mills & Boon romance so very much, you'll really *love* choosing more of your favourite romantic reading from the fascinating, sparkling full-colour pages of "Happy Reading" – the *complete* Mills & Boon catalogue. It not only lists ALL our current top-selling love stories, but it also brings you *advance news* of all our exciting NEW TITLES *plus* lots of super SPECIAL OFFERS! And it comes to you complete with a convenient, easy-to-use DIRECT DELIVERY Order Form.

Imagine! No more *waiting*! No more "sorry – sold out" disappointments! HURRY! Send for *your* FREE Catalogue NOW . . . and ensure a REGULAR supply of all your best-loved Mills & Boon romances this happy, carefree, DIRECT DELIVERY way! But why wait?

Why not – *at the same time* – ORDER NOW a few of the highly recommended titles listed, for your convenience, *overleaf*? It's so simple! Just tick *your* selection(s) on the back and complete the coupon below. Then post *this whole page* – with your remittance (including correct postage and packing) for speedy *by-return* despatch.

✱ POST TO: MILLS & BOON READER SERVICE, P.O. Box 236, Thornton Road, Croydon, Surrey CR9 3RU, England.
Please tick ☑ (as applicable) below:–

☐ Please send me the FREE Mills & Boon Catalogue

☐ As well as my FREE Catalogue please send me the title(s) I have ticked ☑ overleaf

I enclose £................. (No C.O.D.) Please add 25p postage and packing for one book. 15p postage and packing per book for two to nine books (maximum 9 x 15p = £1.35). For TEN books or more FREE postage and packing.

Please write in BLOCK LETTERS below

NAME (Mrs./Miss)..

ADDRESS ....

CITY/TOWN...

COUNTY/COUNTRY...POSTAL/ZIP CODE...................

Readers in South Africa and Zimbabwe please write to:
P.O. BOX 1872, Johannesburg, 2000. S. Africa

ORDER NOW
FOR DIRECT DELIVERY

Choose from this selection of

Mills & Boon 🌳
FAVOURITES
— ALL HIGHLY RECOMMENDED

☐ 1683
WHERE THE WOLF
LEADS
Jane Arbor

☐ 1684
THE DARK OASIS
Margaret Pargeter

☐ 1685
BAREFOOT BRIDE
Dorothy Cork

☐ 1686
A TOUCH OF THE
DEVIL
Anne Weale

☐ 1687
THE SILVER THAW
Betty Neels

☐ 1688
THE DANGEROUS
TIDE
Elizabeth Graham

☐ 1689
MARRIAGE IN HASTE
Sue Peters

☐ 1690
THE TENDER LEAVES
Essie Summers

☐ 1691
LOVE AND NO
MARRIAGE
Roberta Leigh

☐ 1692
THE ICE MAIDEN
Sally Wentworth

☐ 1693
NO PASSING FANCY
Kay Thorpe

☐ 1694
HEART OF STONE
Janet Dailey

☐ 1695
WHEN LIGHTNING
STRIKES
Jane Donnelly

☐ 1696
SHADOW OF DESIRE
Sara Craven

☐ 1697
FEAR OF LOVE
Carole Mortimer

☐ 1698
WIFE BY CONTRACT
Flora Kidd

☐ 1699
WIFE FOR A YEAR
Roberta Leigh

☐ 1700
THE WINDS OF
WINTER
Sandra Field

☐ 1701
FLAMINGO PARK
Margaret Way

☐ 1702
SWEET NOT ALWAYS
Karen van der Zee

ONLY
65p
EACH

SIMPLY TICK √ YOUR SELECTION(S)
ABOVE, THEN JUST COMPLETE AND
POST THE ORDER FORM OVERLEAF